Decision-Making in Geography
a handbook of method and practice
SECOND EDITION

KT-514-327

Keith A Cowlard

Hodder & Stoughton

A MEMBER OF THE HODDER HEADLINE GROUP

ii

Contributors

Dr Peter Allen provided Exercise 30 *Renewing Sea Defences in North East Norfolk* and Exercise 31 *Opening up a Sand and Gravel Quarry*. Dr Peter Shoebridge produced Exercise 32 *International Trade and Development*

Offer

Pebbleshore, the publishers of the SCAMP-2 Census 91 CD-ROM, offer schools and colleges using Decision-Making in Geography a 25% discount on SCAMP-2 or any of its other products.

For details fax Pebbleshore on 01273 479645. Accompany your request with a copy of the book's title page marked with the school / college / library stamp.

Acknowledgements

The author would like to thank the generations of Geography undergraduates who, unwittingly, provided much of the original impetus and content for this text. Julia Morris and Frania Weaver, of Hodder and Stoughton, provided encouragement and help to bring it to final publication.

The support of my family, Margaret, Christopher and Katherine, proved unfailing and invaluable through the many, many hours of reading, writing, typing and deliberation and I thank them all.

I am also indebted to: Rudi Affolter, PhD student, who provided much of the material for Exercise 27 *The 'Environmental' Issue*; John Hume of *Pebbleshore* for software associated with the *SCAMP-2* exercise, Exercise 28.

And to the following for specific sources or for permission to reproduce material:
Pebbleshore for *SCAMP-2*
The Department of the Environment, Transport and the Regions for the Dartford aerial photograph
Ordnance Survey for map extracts
HMSO Social Trends
The Environment Agency
The Geological Survey
Exercise 31 is based on data from Iain Meyer of Brisbane Boys' College, Australia.

British Library Cataloguing in Publication Data
A catalogue record for this title is available from The British Library

ISBN 0 340 691263

First published 1998
Impression number   10 9 8 7 6 5 4 3
Year   2002

Typeset by Fakenham Photosetting Ltd, Fakenham, Norfolk
Printed in Great Britain for Hodder & Stoughton Educational, a division of Hodder Headline Plc, 338 Euston Road, London NW1 3BH
by The Bath Press, Bath

Contents

Preface

'Nothing is more difficult, and therefore more precious, than to be able to decide'
Napoleon I, Maxims, 1804–1815

Geographers have always been concerned to investigate the issues, problems and questions which come from the interactions of people with their environments.

Public curricula and school examinations in the discipline have increasingly focused on these issues, and now give more emphasis to enquiry-based approaches to learning, including the development of appropriate decision-making skills to increase awareness of people–environment problems, and training to enable solutions to be found to those problems.

The DME (Decision Making Exercise) is now an important component of many GCE A-Level and AS-Level examinations, and began with the Schools Council 16–19 Project in the late 1980s. This book addresses current developments in the curriculum and the approaches, techniques and practical examples will provide a vital platform for candidates in these examinations.

The text will also be useful to students at GCSE level, to undergraduates of Geography and related environmental disciplines, and, indeed, to anyone generally interested in people–environment problems.

The open and accessible approach to decision-making techniques presented here will also be of use to anyone simply wishing to improve their individual decision-making abilities.

PART ONE: INTRODUCTION – THE ART OF DECISION-MAKING is the essential introductory reference for decision-makers. It discusses the nature and theory of decisions and presents an easily understood systematic approach to the art of making decisions on geographical topics and issues.

PART TWO: METHOD – THE SCIENCE OF GEOGRAPHICAL DECISION-MAKING explains a wide selection of appropriate decision-making techniques. Each is described in detail, with advice on when to use it, clearly presented step-by-step instructions (with many illustrations) and highlights of the elements to be wary of when using each technique.

PART THREE: PRACTICE – GEOGRAPHICAL DECISION-MAKING EXERCISES consists of ten DMEs – Decision-Making Exercises. They are drawn from a range of geographical topics, regions and scales, and each covers some section of the public examination curriculum within a people–environment question, problem or issue. They are chosen to provide material for individual examination practice and for extended group decision-making activity.

Note: *the exercises, though based on actual places, data, projects and cases, may have some details altered and names changed. Some scenarios are fictitious and no attribution to real projects, people, plans or policies should be made for any of the exercises.*

A Note on the Second Edition
The first edition of this book was published in 1990 and was extremely well-received.

The opportunity for a second edition has allowed the updating of virtually all of the content, the addition of many new techniques, including those related to information technology, evaluation, and remote sensing, together with deeper explanation of some techniques presented more briefly in the first edition. There is a completely new set of decision-making exercises.

The now extensively expanded list of techniques is still as concisely and simply explained as in the first edition, and readers will find all of the methods just as readily useable. The originally successful format of description, method and watchpoints has been retained for the techniques sections.

The new set of DMEs has been chosen to reflect changes in national school curriculum and in the range of topics, levels and regions to be covered in public examinations since the first edition, as well as the broad scope of modern geography.

PART ONE

INTRODUCTION – THE ART OF DECISION-MAKING

1 | What is Decision-Making?

Multitudes, multitudes in the valley of decision....
Joel, Chapter 3, Verse 14

When you think about it, we spend most of our lives making decisions – we are all decision-makers. You chose to read this text, perhaps because you reasoned that it might improve your knowledge of decision-making, make you more decisive, or you estimated that it might improve your chances of examination success. The world statesman resolves to follow a course of action, from the selection of alternatives determined by his advisers, in an attempt to change a global political situation. The businesswoman concludes that she must adjudicate in the controversy over the site of the new factory because there is no more time to gather information. The town council, split by political beliefs and public opinion, is swayed by the measured arguments of its valued planning team, and makes up its mind. The judge settles a question by determining the verdict in an enquiry into prejudice and discrimination. After going through the process of comparing your options and evaluating today's weather predictions, you settled on the clothes to wear for the day. Then you made the decision to have tea or coffee for breakfast....

Decision-making is so much a part of life at all levels, that we rarely think about how we make our decisions or how we might make good and better decisions. We all make decisions, we all talk about decisions and we all suffer the consequences of decisions, yet few of us have received any training in the process of making decisions or in the methods by which we can tackle real-world problems and produce effective and justifiable decisions.

All decision-making involves the investigation, comparison and evaluation of information and of alternative decisions, and there are many ways to approach these tasks and to make the required choices. Just look at the quotation and the first paragraph above: they contain over forty words or phrases that we commonly use to describe something to do with decision-making:

> *problem, chose, perhaps, reasoned, might, knowledge, decisive, estimated, chances, examination, resolves, course of action, selection, alternatives, determined, advisers, attempt to change, concludes, adjudicate, controversy, information, beliefs, opinion, measured, arguments, valued, planning, makes up its mind, judge, question, determining, verdict, enquiry, discrimination, process, comparing, options, evaluating, predictions, settled, made the decision.*

Effective decisions for complex problems can best be achieved through a systematic approach to the method and practice of decision-making. We begin with a working definition of our subject, chosen from amongst the many options listed from our first paragraph:

> *DECISION-MAKING IS THE PROCESS OF EVALUATING THE ALTERNATIVES AND CHOOSING A COURSE OF ACTION IN ORDER TO SOLVE A PROBLEM.*

2 | What is Geographical Decision-Making?

We can broadly define Geography as 'the study of the earth's surface as the environment of people'. From this we can describe specifically geographical problems as 'those problems, issues and questions which are the result of the interrelationships between people and their environments'.

Geography is thus concerned about the future of the world at all levels and the quality of the people–environment relationship. The subject can make distinctive contributions to environmental understanding and management, and the geographical decision-maker may be required to

Geographical Decision-Making and the People – Environment Relationship

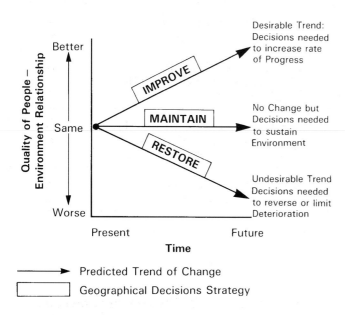

Figure 2.1

work anywhere within the range of strategies to improve, maintain or restore the people-environment relationship (Figure 2.1).

Typically, geographical problems may involve ecological issues (relationships between people and physical environments) and/or locational issues (relationships between people and spatial environments), and frequently require the decision-maker to work with:

- complex relationships of issues, options and evidence

- uncertainty about the future

- wide range of physical and human factors

- irrational human behaviour

- wide-ranging values held by individuals or groups affected

- rapidly changing situations

- imperfect or incomplete evidence

- conflicting objectives and viewpoints

- potentially wide impacts of decisions

- more than one decision at a time

- varied interests, requiring value-judgements

- both spatial and temporal issues – location and time elements

- a range of scales from local to regional to national to international to global

- short and long term views.

Geographical decision-making is thus the fascinating quest to make sense of, and resolve, the complicated problems which can arise from people–environment relationships. This can be achieved through a systematic approach which we can now define as:

> **GEOGRAPHICAL DECISION-MAKING IS THE SYSTEMATIC PROCESS OF EVALUATING THE ALTERNATIVES AND CHOOSING A COURSE OF ACTION IN ORDER TO SOLVE A GEOGRAPHICAL PROBLEM.**

3 The Systematic Approach to Decision-Making

'Fortune favours the prepared mind'

Louis Pasteur

'If you don't know where you are going, you will probably end up somewhere else'

L J Peter

There are many kinds of decision. There is the uncomplicated, subjective decision made on the basis of a simple hunch or intuitive feeling at one end of the scale, and at the other there is the complicated, objective decision made with the help of a computer. Neither approach is satisfactory. Geographical decisions should not be just a hunch,

nor a mechanical, automatic result. They can best be reached by adopting a systematic approach, following a methodical path, one stage at a time. Such a systematic approach has advantages in that it:

- ensures that all necessary tasks are accomplished without omission

- enables complex evidence to be handled easily

- gives confidence to tackle any problem

- gives a clear framework which ensures no effort is wasted by duplication

The Systematic Approach to Geographical Decision-Making

FOCUS	QUESTION	STAGE	ACTION	MNEMONIC
THE PROBLEM	What is the problem and what must be achieved?	1 2	**I**DENTIFY THE PROBLEM **F**IX THE OBJECTIVES	**I** **F**
THE EVIDENCE	What is the evidence and what does it show?	3 4 5	**N**OTE THE EVIDENCE **O**RGANIZE THE INFORMATION **T**EST THE DATA	**N** **O** **T**
THE ALTERNATIVES	What are the alternatives and which one is best?	6 7 8	**G**ENERATE THE ALTERNATIVES **E**VALUATE THE OPTIONS **T**ARGET THE BEST CHOICE	**G** **E** **T**
THE DECISION	What decision ought to be taken?	9 10	**M**AKE THE DECISION **E**XPLAIN THE RESULT	**M** **E**

Figure 3.1

- makes it easier to apply the right techniques, and at the correct time
- improves the quality of decisions by making it easier to see how a choice was made
- helps to structure and understand the problem itself
- the logical sequence helps presentation, since the process is efficiently recorded
- careful planning can result in better decisions.

The systematic approach is not an 'answer machine' and does not replace common sense, personal judgement, empathy or argument, but what it does, is to set out a logical route to effective decision-making. There is no such thing as a perfect decision – but a systematic approach gives us the best chance of designing the best possible solution to the problem. The geographical decision-maker should thoroughly understand the stages in the process, learn the sequence and be able to apply it efficiently when required.

The *systematic approach to geographical decision-making* is set out in Figure 3.1. The broad pattern is a shift of *focus*:

THE PROBLEM
↓
THE EVIDENCE
↓
THE ALTERNATIVES
↓
THE DECISION

to answer the *questions*:

What is the PROBLEM and what must be achieved?
↓
What is the EVIDENCE and what does it show?
↓
What are the ALTERNATIVES and which is best?
↓
What DECISION ought to be taken?

by carrying out a sequence of *actions*, each of which identifies a distinct stage in the systematic approach to geographical decision-making.

The Problem

STAGE 1   *Identify the problem*

Here the aim is to achieve awareness of the nature of the problem, issue or question that is to be resolved, by identifying that a problem does, indeed, exist and then describing it clearly and unambiguously:

What is wrong or in need of action?

What are the central issues?

Where is the problem and what is the geographical nature of it?

STAGE 2   *Fix the objectives*

Now the goals, aims or objectives must be clarified and precisely defined:

   What are you being asked to do?

   What must be achieved by decision?

   What are the major obstacles to achieving the objectives?

   What criteria could be used to measure a decision against the objectives?

   By now the decision-maker has detected the problem to be investigated and clearly defined both the problem and objectives. This gives a solid base and clear direction for the next stages, helps to concentrate ideas on the important aspects and may begin to suggest the evidence and techniques to be used in later analysis.

The Evidence

STAGE 3   *Note the evidence*

Here the evidence is assembled and inspected to note its general nature and extent, and to identify that which can be used, any which needs reorganising before use, and any gaps there might be in the data. Note the types of evidence available – facts, values, knowledge or experience – and begin to list the possibilities of using them in later analysis. Evaluate the evidence and identify inaccuracy, bias or other characteristics which you must be wary of when using the data.

STAGE 4   *Organize the information*

Now the first work is done on the evidence to organize it, refine it and generally translate it into more usable forms. This involves selecting, tabulating, classifying, summarizing, scaling and reducing information into more manageable and understandable formats in order to proceed to the next stage.

STAGE 5   *Test the data*

Here detailed analysis of the evidence is undertaken to detect relationships and trends, compute results, make predictions and draw conclusions. By now the decision-maker has a clear picture of exactly what the evidence tells about the problem and is in a position to turn to the alternatives.

The Alternatives

STAGE 6   *Generate the alternatives*

Now the range of alternative answers to solve the problem is considered and each option is described in detail. All possible choices should be offered, and this need not exclude the 'do nothing' option.

STAGE 7   *Evaluate the options*

Here the alternatives are individually assessed to gauge their ability to solve the problem. Each is examined on its advantages, disadvantages and consequences, and these are measured against its effectiveness in meeting the original objectives.

STAGE 8   *Target the best choice*

Now the relative value of each option is compared with the others, in order to isolate the one which appears to be the best and most effective choice to solve the problem. Which is best? What makes it the best? The decision-maker has used all the evidence and considered all the possibilities and can now make the decision.

The Decision

STAGE 9   *Make the decision*

Based on the results of the enquiry and considering all the evidence, what ought to be done? Make up your mind and be prepared to stand by your decision.

STAGE 10   *Explain the result*

Presenting and explaining the decision is perhaps one of the most important stages. If the systematic approach has been followed, the enquiries should already be in a suitable state to be drawn together and communicated as a well-argued decision report. Part of this explanation should look at the consequences of the decision – every decision has consequences!

   To help you to remember the systematic approach, Figure 3.1 also includes a *mnemonic*, derived from the initial letter of the first word of each stage of the process:

IF NOT GET ME!

A decision was once described as 'action that must be taken when an answer does not immediately suggest itself'. So, **IF** an answer does **NOT** suggest itself – **GET ME**!

Decision-Making and Problem-Solving

Strictly speaking, decision-making is not the same as problem-solving, since the decision-maker stops at Stage 10 of the process, having made the recommendations for action. Problem-solving puts the decisions into effect and monitors the consequences, thus adding two further stages.

STAGE 11   *Implement the plan*

Here the decision is actually carried out in practice and applied to the environment in question.

STAGE 12   *Trace the progress*

Now the effectiveness of the decision is assessed by monitoring future changes in the environment as they happen. In turn, this may reveal further

problems and so take us back to Stage 1. The decision-maker attempts to predict the consequences of the decision; the problem-solver actually traces these consequences (Figure 3.2). For the problem-solver, the mnemonic becomes:

IF NOT GET ME IT!

Decision-Making and Problem Solving

STAGE	ACTION	MNEMONIC	DECISION MAKING	PROBLEM SOLVING
1	IDENTIFY the problem	I		
2	FIX the objectives	F		
3	NOTE the evidence	N		
4	ORGANIZE the information	O		
5	TEST the data	T		
6	GENERATE the alternatives	G		
7	EVALUATE the options	E		
8	TARGET the best choice	T		
9	MAKE the decision	M		
10	EXPLAIN the result	E		
11	IMPLEMENT THE PLAN	I		
12	TRACE THE PROGRESS	T		

Figure 3.2

4   *Evidence: The Decision-Maker's Key Resource*

Evidence may be defined as the total set of information at the disposal of the decision-maker, including the skills necessary for its use. It is therefore the key resource at all stages of the decision-making process and involves all the 'ammunition' that the decision-maker can bring to bear on the problem.

The quality of evidence

Ideally, the decision-maker hopes to have good-quality evidence in abundant supply. Frequently, the evidence will be lacking in some way, and, as far as possible, the decision-maker would hope to enhance its quality and usefulness at Stage 4, otherwise decisions will be more difficult (Figure 4.1).

Evidence : Good vs Poor

GOOD EVIDENCE IS	POOR EVIDENCE IS
Available	Not available
In right form	In wrong form
Comprehensive	Incomplete
Up to date	Out of date
Accurate	Inaccurate
Unbiased	Biased
Relevant	Irrelevant
Unique	Duplicated
Consistent	Inconsistent
Understandable	Unclear
Mappable	Unmappable
Scaled	Unscaled
Evaluated	Not evaluated
Classified	Unclassified
Organised	Unorganised
Unambiguous	Ambiguous
Non-conflicting	Conflicting
Justifiable	Assumed
Precise	Vague
Uncomplicated	Complex
Used	Unused
Analysed	Not Analysed
Interpreted	Uninterpreted
Known	Unknown
WHAT THE DECISION-MAKER HOPES TO HAVE	WHAT THE DECISION-MAKER OFTEN GETS

THE ANSWER?

THE DECISION-MAKERS AIM:

CONVERT POOR TO GOOD

Figure 4.1

The type of evidence

The following may be given or collected:

- *Facts* Specific to the problem, these are measurable, often precise truths or figures that rely on no assumptions and are generally amenable to a wide range of analytical techniques. They are often used to test feasibility and answer the question, 'Is the decision practical?' Facts are objective evidence, sometimes misleadingly called 'geographical factors'.

- *Values* Specific to the problem, these are opinions, views, attitudes, prejudices, assumptions and interpretations that are difficult to measure, but are important influences on the decision-making process. They are often used to test desirability and answer the question, 'Is the decision right?' Values are subjective evidence and require empathic understanding.

The decision-maker should also recognise that he or she brings an individual personality and value-system to the problem and this may influence the use of all kinds of evidence. The following may be brought to the problem by the decision-maker:

- *Knowledge* Additional to the evidence given with the problem, this is the decision-maker's familiarity with similar areas or topics, geographical theories or models, general relevant concepts or data and includes any general geographical knowledge or skills of relevance to the problem.

- *Experience* Additional to the evidence given with the problem, this is the decision-maker's expertise in the decision-making process, ability to use the techniques of decision-making and experience of making decisions in the past.

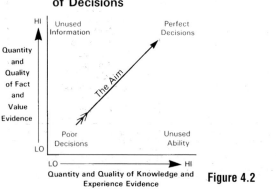

Types of Evidence and Quality of Decisions

Figure 4.2

Under examination conditions, the facts and values will be given to you. Only the knowledge and experience (and your own value system) are supplied by you, hence diligent study to improve these two (Figure 4.2) is the most effective aim for perfect decision-making!

Obtain as much experience as you can in geographical decision-making. The exercises in this book cover a broad range of geographical issues and problems and require the use of most of the techniques explained in Part One. Such practice will develop in you the three classic goals:

- Build up your *skills acquisition* to enable you to select and properly carry out the appropriate technical procedures for all kinds of decisions, knowing when to use each, what they do and do not do, and how to do it.

- Widen your *knowledge acquisition* so that you can easily and progressively get better at decisions and solving complex problems, from experiencing many different scenarios in detail.

- Increase what is called your *cognitive level* so that you can broaden your general level of understanding of geographical issues and problems by exploring them further, apply your general geographical knowledge of theory, process and information, and develop new hypotheses or procedures to solve particular problems.

The form of evidence

The geographical decision-maker should be able to use evidence in any form, and be aware of the techniques available to deal with each of them. They may be:

numerical – in number form. These may be, from richest to poorest data:

- ratio data, measured on a continuous scale with an absolute zero (such as age, area, height or degrees kelvin, where negative numbers are not meaningful).

- interval data, measured on a continuous scale with no real zero (such as degrees Fahrenheit).

- ordinal data, measured in groups or categories with an implied scale or ranking (small, medium and large incomes, or opinion survey results).

Data Level	Usefulness	Measurement Scale	Measurement Character	Examples
Ratio	Best/Richest	Continuous	Categories and ranks and equal intervals and absolute zero	Areas, °Kelvin
Interval		Continuous	Categories and ranks and equal intervals	°Fahrenheit
Ordinal		Categories	Categories and ranks	Opinion surveys, Income levels
Nominal	Worst/Poorest	Categories	Categories only	Soil type, Ethnic Group

Figure 4.3 The Usefulness of Numerical Evidence

- nominal data, measured in groups or categories only (such as gender, nationality, soil or rock type), with no quantification of the categories.

Numerical data in the higher level, richer types has the potential to give you more information and to allow you to use more sophisticated analytical techniques (Figure 4.3).

literal – in written-word form. These may be:

- published, so open to public scrutiny and checking

- unpublished, not open to public scrutiny so you may possibly need to be more wary

- private written sources, not produced by an official body

- official written sources, produced by an official body.

See Section 22 for how to handle these source materials.

graphical – in chart, picture, diagrammatic or map form.
See Sections 12, 14 and 22 on how to handle these sources.

articulated – in spoken form.
See Section 20 on how to handle this evidence.

The uncertainties and risks with evidence

Geographical problems frequently involve evidence that is difficult to measure and so predict, and options whose outcomes may not be easily described. We often have to use a wide range of evidence types that will not give us exact and predictable outcomes and, in making our decisions, we have to deal with the *uncertainties* and *risks* associated with our problem.

Uncertainty arises because we have no absolute way of predicting results from our decisions, and it can range from:

- *Certain predictability*: where the outcomes of all the alternatives are known for certain, and we have few problems in making our decision, to:

- *Uncertain predictability*: where none of the outcomes of the alternatives are known and we cannot reach a decision simply without using our experience, intuition or guesswork.

Risk has a more precise meaning than uncertainty, because it involves us measuring or quantifying the level of uncertainty, so that the probabilities of the outcomes are known and we can then make confident decisions. The decision-maker finds the job easiest with 'certain' evidence, and hardest with 'uncertain', and many techniques use the probabilities of risk.

So, evidence is the key resource at all stages of the systematic approach and the geographical decision-maker has a considerable armoury of evidence with which to tackle problems (Figure 4.4). Understanding the armoury of *type, form and risk* ensures the selection of the correct techniques and, ultimately, the most effective decision-making.

The Evidence

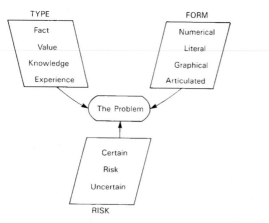

Figure 4.4

Utility and decision strategies

Utility is the value, desirability or satisfaction derived from the outcome of a decision. It is usually expressed as a number on a scale between 0 and 100 and measures the attractiveness of the pay-off from a particular decision.

It is often thought that the decision-maker always aims to maximize the 'expected utility', and many geographical theories are based on the behaviour of maximizing 'economic-man'. In reality, decision-makers are frequently satisfied with a lesser utility.

Sometimes it is possible to calculate the utility of a particular choice to all the individuals or groups that will be affected, in order to identify the best action for everyone. At other times, it may be that one individual's or group's utility is more important.

Utility, Risk and Decision Strategies

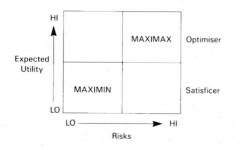

Figure 4.5

The geographical decision-maker should consider the appropriate strategy for each problem as it arises. The 'optimiser' is the idealist, continually striving for the highest expected utility. The 'maximax' decision-maker is the gambler who tries to obtain the maximum utility, even if it means running the highest risk of losing it all (Figure 4.5).

The 'satisficer' is the realist who is content with a lower utility to give a decision that is 'good enough', and the 'maximin' decision-maker is the pessimist who chooses the lesser utility because that minimizes the risks, even though it cannot give the best return. For further explanations see Section 10.

SWOT Analysis

'SWOT' analysis is a process which looks at the:

- **S**trengths
- **W**eaknesses
- **O**pportunities and
- **T**hreats

associated with a problem, scenario, decision, policy or even a person.

SWOT is a good *mnemonic* (from the first letter of each element) to point you towards the key characteristics of your problem. It is therefore useful at many stages during the decision-making process. For example, we might be asked to make a decision about local authority policy with regard to the wildlife support in towns that comes from people's private gardens, so we might use SWOT early on, to identify:

Strengths:

- Private gardens cover a large proportion of local authority area
- Involve private money, not public
- Diverse in nature, so provide a variety of habitats for flora and fauna

Weaknesses:

- No direct investment control by the council
- No control over planting by the council
- Have to resort to encouragement and incentives to change anything

Opportunities:

- Additional planting if supply plants at discount to residents

- Encouragement of composting by supplying bins at discount

- Educate on wildlife gardening, adults and in schools

- Publicise initiatives in local press

Threats:

- Uncontrolled use of pesticides, insecticides in private gardens

- Overtidiness for wildlife

- Lack of council finance to publicise initiatives.

5   *The Mind of the Decision-Maker*

'It is the mind which creates the world about us, and even though we stand side by side in the same meadow, my eyes will never see what is beheld by yours, my heart will never stir to the emotions with which yours is touched.'

G Gissing

'Whenever decisions are made strictly on the basis of bottom-line arithmetic, human beings get crunched along with the numbers'

T Horton

As a decision-maker you have your own mind and personality, with their particular mixtures of culture, values, imagination, prejudice, motivation and emotion. It is hardly surprising, therefore, that a decision can appear wrong, or irrational, or unwise to you, yet at the same time be seen as totally acceptable to others.

Although systematic and objective approaches and techniques are important, we should never use these means alone to arrive at a decision. We are dealing with people–environment relationships and these are rarely simple and often involve many differing individuals or groups that will be affected by our decision.

We have to use the best problem-solving machine ever produced – our own minds:

- Know your own mind: examine your personal feelings over the given problem and ask yourself if these feelings, values, or attitudes are relevant and if they will affect your judgement. If they will, should you let them? Can you justify them with the evidence? Should you be approaching the problem from a different angle?

- Use all of your mental faculties: your **perceptive abilities**, comprising: *sensations* (your five senses of sight, hearing, touch, smell and taste); *intuition* (perceiving possibilities in a situation, using the unconscious mind). Your **judgement abilities**, comprising: *feelings* (subjective evaluations, value judgements); *thoughts* (rational reasoning with analysis and logic).

- Know the minds of others: examine other people's opinions and motives and ask yourself if these are relevant, and if they are, which views should be seen as more important? Can you support this from the evidence? Should any of these views override your own personal views?

- Use your empathy: if you *sympathise*, you appreciate other people's feelings, but if you *empathise*, you go further to get close to feeling and thinking exactly as they would in their circumstances. Empathy can be defined as responding with heart, feelings, soul and passion – frequently, we are asked, implicitly or explicitly, to 'empathise', to try to put ourselves in other's shoes and see things from their perspective and values. This can be very important if that individual's or group's lifestyles are very different from our own, and we must beware of putting our own cultural, social or national perspectives where they are not warranted. If you are put into a role in the decision-making exercise, then empathise with that role. If you have data from other cultures or world regions, try to put yourself there and think how people living there, not here, would react, feel about and approach the decision. What must it be like to actually be there? Understanding and using 'values positions' is now specifically used as one of the criteria of assessment of the examination DME.

- Understand how facts can be differently interpreted in other minds: increased traffic flow in a road-widening scheme might be taken as clear evidence of economic progress by the businesswoman, yet equally 'correctly' as evidence of a worsening environment by the conservationist or as a waste of resources by the tax payer.

- Know that our individual personalities can have an important role to play in our final decisions. Are you, an *analyser* (you split problems into components and tend to use logic); or a *synthesiser* (you think more in wholes and are best piecing things together to get an overview), or even a *valuer* (you judge everything on its comparative significance or importance)?

In truth, we really need a little bit of all of these approaches to be good decision-makers.

- Everyone's bias is different. Some tackle decision-making problems from an economic perspective, others from sociological, political, theoretical, methodological, mathematical or religious standpoints, as long as we are aware of our own natures, then we ought to be able to temper our own prejudices and biases to arrive at reasonable decisions.

- Decisions may be made for unfortunate reasons of emotional reaction, prejudice, habit, bias, or even pure serendipity (simple chance, like tossing a coin) and different people are, by nature, optimistic or pessimistic in their approaches to life. All of these can affect decision-making and we should be aware of the dangers in all of them.

- Above all, listen to your own mind: do not be afraid to use your intuition and opinions, because this can result in creative decision-making. Try to balance your systematic judgement processes with your perception and empathy. Be prepared to stand by your views and always support them from the evidence.

6   *The Secrets of Success*

1 Learn and use the systematic approach to geographical decision-making: it provides the necessary ingredients to make effective decisions and to pass decision-making examinations.

2 The final decision-report should follow the exact requirements of the exercise given, but as a general guide ensure that you:

- show that you have followed a systematic and logical procedure to arrive at your decision
- state the objectives and clearly identify the problems
- show ability to use appropriate techniques and know their limitations
- properly evaluate the evidence and show appreciation of the ways that values influence your results
- can use appropriate techniques to analyse information and generate alternatives, and clearly present them
- show that you can evaluate options and effectively target the best solution
- fully and clearly justify the recommendations, showing how you arrived at them

- use effective methods to present the decision including annotated charts and maps, analysis and argument
- if you become stuck and find yourself drowning in the problem, use the emergency *lifebelt questions* to prompt the next action (Figure 6.1)
- practice decision-making to increase knowledge and experience
- have the courage to stand by your decisions.

3 Aim to make your report as readable and understandable as possible:

- use short, uncomplicated sentences – simple is always best
- avoid jargon, technical terms and slang, use familiar words
- use subheadings, bullet and number listings freely
- do not be sloppy or inexact in your statements and avoid ambiguity
- explain carefully how you arrived at your decision
- give all supporting evidence and analyses

Lifebelt Questions

QUESTION	TO DO?	WHY?	ELSE?	OUGHT?
WHAT?	IS TO BE DONE?	WHY DO IT?	WHAT ELSE COULD BE DONE?	WHAT OUGHT TO BE DONE?
HOW?	TO DO IT?	WHY DO IT THAT WAY?	HOW ELSE COULD IT BE DONE?	HOW OUGHT IT BE DONE?
WHERE?	TO DO IT?	WHY DO IT THERE?	WHERE ELSE COULD IT BE DONE?	WHERE OUGHT IT BE DONE?
WHEN?	TO DO IT?	WHY DO IT THEN?	WHEN ELSE COULD IT BE DONE?	WHEN OUGHT IT BE DONE?
WHO?	TO DO IT?	WHY SHOULD X DO IT?	WHO ELSE COULD DO IT?	WHO OUGHT TO DO IT?

Figure 6.1

- use appropriate illustrations
- avoid emotive explanations
- be logical in ordering your response
- write clearly and concisely, using correct spelling and grammar
- have a clear conclusion.

4 When marking, examiners will broadly look for:

- quality of argument
  - addressing the questions
  - logically developed
  - convincing
  - presented enthusiastically

- well-structured reports
  - with introduction, main text and conclusion

- use of evidence
  - relevant material
  - relevant techniques
  - depth of analysis
  - quality of evidence
  - use to support decision

- presentation
  - accurate use of evidence
  - good examples
  - effective use of illustrations

- writing
  - fluent and succinct
  - correct spelling, punctuation and grammar
  - legible
  - concise, not too long.

> **The DME (Decision Making Exercise) Guidance for the 16–19 Project A-Level, cites the following criteria as being used to mark the reports. Typically, around 16 per cent of the total marks for a whole Geography A-Level will come from the DME. These are made up as follows:**
>
> 1 The identification of the problem and use of a clear sequence of enquiry – 16%
> 2 The selection and application of a technique or techniques appropriate to the issue – 28%
> 3 The appreciation of values positions and the steps followed in values clarification – 16%
> 4 The presentation of a clear statement of alternative solutions and likely consequences – 20%
> 5 The quality of reporting and justifying recommendations – 20%

PART TWO

METHOD – THE SCIENCE OF GEOGRAPHICAL DECISION-MAKING

7 *The Techniques of Geographical Decision-Making*

The techniques which follow will provide a sound basis for approaching all geographical problems. Each technique may be used at most stages of the systematic approach and can be adapted for a wide range of geographical problems.

The techniques have been simplified for the purposes of this text. Readers requiring a deeper knowledge of particular techniques should refer to more advanced texts in decision-making (see the bibliography).

Every technique is explained through: a brief *description* of its nature, uses and background, an explanation of the *method* of use, clearly explained step by step and illustrated where appropriate; a note of particular *watchpoints* to guarantee success. These:

- ensure that you select the correct technique and are aware of its limitations when you use it

- help you to evaluate material presented to you which uses these techniques in analysing or presenting the information.

8 *Tabulation*

In geographical decision-making problems the information can often be in the form of large and complex reference tables, with detailed figures in a comprehensive database, or may be given as an unclassified group of differing information sets that require some sorting and conversion before they can be used. The problem for the decision-maker is that not all of the information may be needed, there may be incompatible units used for numerical data and the information or table may not be arranged in the clearest fashion.

The purpose of tabulation is to organize the information or redesign the table to make the relevant elements clearer and to make them easier to work with, or to produce a table of your own in your presentation report. It is common in DMEs to have to amalgamate data from a number of the given sources into a single table before it begins to make sense.

Method

Much will depend on the actual problem being analysed, but the illustration (Figure 8.1) suggests a range of ways in which information presented in tables can be made clearer. The problem was to find out if Wakefield township had any unusual changes in its population between 1881 and 1901. The original information was detailed and poorly presented. The improved table (Figure 8.1i) shows how simply redrawing, simplifying, converting to common units and calculating percentages and totals can help to solve our problem.

The process may involve:

- collecting the data sets together for a single table and checking them for compatibility

Improving Tables

The original table

POPULATION 1881-1901

	1881	1891	1901
YORKSHIRE	2886536	3208502	3584675
ALVERTHORPE	10486	12086	13475
HORBURY	5050	5676	6736
STANLEY	13431	15576	18033
WEST RIDING	2165056	2429632	2733688
WAKEFIELD	22173	23315	24107

Figure 8.1

The improved table

WAKEFIELD: COMPARATIVE POPULATION CHANGE 1881–1901

Re-orient table:
change in time important – easier to add and compare vertically

Figures vertical in line easier to read

POPULATION:	WAKEFIELD	REST OF PARISH	WEST RIDING	YORKSHIRE
1881	22,200	23,900	2,165,100	2,886,500
1891	23,300	33,300	2,429,600	3,208,500
1901	24,100	38,200	2,733,700	3,584,700
POPULATION CHANGE 1881–1901	1,900	14,300	586,600	698,200

Rounded figures if detail not important

Double lines or spaces to highlight totals

Normal punctuation makes size of number easier

Wakefield the focus put first and larger case

Spaces to separate

Two tables – % conversion easier guide

% CHANGE:	WAKEFIELD	REST OF PARISH	WEST RIDING	YORKSHIRE
1881–1891	5	39	12	11
1891–1901	3	15	13	12
% CHANGE 1881–1901	9	59	26	24

In logical rank order left to right township – parish – riding – county

No spurious precision from decimal points – simple comparisons easier with simple figures

Rest of parish more important than townships – collapse categories to simplify

Double lines (or spaces) separate whole parish (Wakefield and Rest of parish) from others

Calculate rows and/or column totals

Classes to be directly compared to adjacent columns

Figure 8.1i

- rewriting data or re-presenting in a more convenient form

- selecting appropriate groups or subsets of the information to present in table form

- converting information to common or understandable units – perhaps by converting all information to a single unit format, or calculating percentages rather than giving raw figures

- re-orienting tables so that proper comparisons of information can be made:

  - presenting the larger categories first and the smallest last – we can understand tables better if they are simple and logical. A good rule is: largest top and left
  - if you need to compare figures by dates, then it is easier if the date information is down the left hand column, as it is always easier to compare figures in columns than figures in rows
  - collapsing rows or columns if that shows comparisons better, or putting data you want to compare next to each other in the table

- simplifying: rounding figures off so that it is easier to see elements and spurious exactness is eliminated. The usual rule is that a fraction or decimal of less than half of one is rounded down, if more than half of one, it is rounded up

- calculating simple totals from the rows and columns, as a focus for your information

- spacing the table so that it is easier to read: using lines or blank lines to lead the eye to the important information and highlighting the more important information

- giving clear titles to tables, and to their rows and columns.

Wakefield township was surrounded by the townships of Alverthorpe, Horbury and Stanley. Together, they comprised the parish which was situated in West Riding, one of the three subdivisions of the county of Yorkshire.

It is made clear in the revised table that Wakefield township was growing more slowly than its suburbs. The parish as a whole declined from 1881 to 1901 in rate of change, while the Riding and County rates accelerated.

Watchpoints on tabulation

1 Most useful where much of the information is in the form of complex reference tables or lists of figures, or is simply not in a format to help the decision.

2 Can take time, so think carefully about whether the time spent will be adequately rewarded (tables are usually much quicker to produce and use than charts).

3 Be watchful for incomplete data sets, data given for irregular time periods and incompatible measurement units when making comparisons or conclusions.

4 Check all totals in tables or lists – do not accept correctness until you have added them up yourself.

5 Sometimes tables or data sets come with footnotes, which give insights into how the data was collected, or may provide clues to the possible deficiencies in the information.

6 Much depends on what you want to use the table for:

   - If you want to use a complex table with detailed figures for *reference purposes*, then you must annotate it, or explain its main elements in words alongside the table.
   - If you want to use a table for *presentation or demonstration*, then both the table and the data must be simple and the table should still have a brief written summary to provide impact.

7 Tabulation can:

   a) Help information processing by highlighting the essentials.
   b) Make clearer the conclusions that you may be able to draw from the data.
   c) Help decision presentation – since clear tables can show clear, incisive decision-making!
   d) Be most useful with numerical data and specific amounts, rather than qualitative data or less detailed amounts, where charts may be more useful.

8 Remember: most numbers or figures are meaningless on their own – it is only when they are compared to other numbers or figures that the picture emerges, and that is where a well prepared table is most useful.

9 Scaling

Information which comes in quantitative or numerical form (e.g. population, pebble counts or trade figures) can be relatively easily processed, since it already has the basis of a ranking or categorization system in its data. Much geographical information is not so well defined and it may be qualitative, involve opinions or other less easily measured variables.

Scaling exists to try to incorporate some kind of standard structure or relative positioning to the data, so that it can be compared with other data and measured, and so that we can appraise the information and compare alternatives. It therefore helps us to decide what to do by identifying and measuring all factors and then allowing some kind of scalar redefinition to provide a basis for employing more objective decision-making methods.

Most methods involve the decision-maker in personal, subjective ranking or measuring and so may introduce bias to the analysis. However, with complex problems, some relative measurement may be essential to find a way through the complexity and, as long as we recognize the limitations to scaling, it is a useful tool for decision-making. The methods use two elements of scaling:

- *Ranking* is the way we introduce structure to the factors we feel are relevant to the problem, by placing them in some order of priority, preference or importance.

- *Rating* is when we then add scores to the factors to measure or weight their priority, preference or importance, and so give us relative numbers with which to analyse further.

Methods

A Nominal Scaling

Nominal data is that which is categorical and simply measured by being placed in a group (see Figure 4.3). Inclusion in a category is determined by the existence or non-existence of some factor. The example shows simple ranking of Yes/No answers. As the data is nominal, there can be no attempt at a rating scale or at quantifying the information any further. The ranks are then analysed by simply adding up the number of Yes and No answers in order to compare the options, as in the example of a road improvement scheme (Figure 9.1).

B Ordinal Scaling

Ordinal data is that which is categorical, but is also measured against some kind of implied scale (it has a form of ranking of its own). Information is placed in order or ranked on some criterion (Figure 9.2). This is useful where absolute values are not known, but relative positions on some defined scale can be identified, so that the factors can be rated against each other. Here the Yes/No answers have been converted to an ascending ordinal scale which runs from 'low priority' to 'high priority' via 'below average' and 'above average' – a scale without exact definition and where the most precision we can use is to put the data into a number of boxes or groupings and rate them. These rated totals then give a different answer from Figure 9.1.

Nominal Scaling

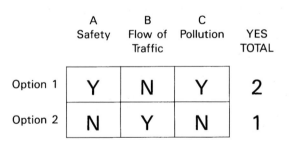

	A Safety	B Flow of Traffic	C Pollution	YES TOTAL
Option 1	Y	N	Y	2
Option 2	N	Y	N	1

Y = Yes, objective met
N = No, objective not met

Figure 9.1

Ordinal Scaling

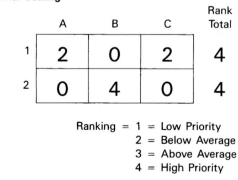

	A	B	C	Rank Total
1	2	0	2	4
2	0	4	0	4

Ranking = 1 = Low Priority
2 = Below Average
3 = Above Average
4 = High Priority

Figure 9.2

C Weighted Scaling

Nominal and ordinal scales may, when appropriate, be rated more precisely by the addition of weighting. This then incorporates a relative rating along one or both of the matrix dimensions (Figure 9.3). The example weights the objectives from Figure 9.2 on the perceived importance of each to the decision.

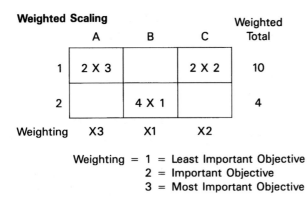

Weighted Scaling

	A	B	C	Weighted Total
1	2 X 3		2 X 2	10
2		4 X 1		4
Weighting	X3	X1	X2	

Weighting = 1 = Least Important Objective
2 = Important Objective
3 = Most Important Objective

Figure 9.3

D Utility or Probability Scaling

We might subjectively try to guess the utility or pay-off for a decision option, or estimate the probability of the likelihood of events. Utility or probability scaling tries to put some numerical value on that guess.

1 Subjectively rank the utility or likelihood on a wide scale, say, from 100 = the best utility, or absolute certainty, down to 0 = the worst utility or absolute uncertainty.

2 Convert to a rated probability. A utility of 50 would mean that 50 times out of 100 we expect it to pay off or happen, so probability (p) = 50, divided by 100 = 0.5.

3 Probabilities must sum to 1: if p = 1 this is absolute certainty, if p = 0 it will never happen.

4 This can then be used to analyse the data:

   • The probability that either of two events will occur is the *sum* of their respective probabilities.
   • The probability that both of two independent events will occur is the *product* of their probabilities.

(For an example of the use of probability scaling see Section 15)

E Bipolar Scaling

Frequently used in questionnaire surveys, this is the technique which scales along a continuous line from two extremes of a variable. It is useful for qualitative data and may be used where it is difficult to put an exact figure on data, but it can be difficult to interpret. Figure 9.4 shows a bipolar survey described by a profile chart, using the shape of the lines and the marginal totals as a rating measurement.

F Forcefield Scaling

A graphical method to show the balance between the pro- (advantage) and con- (disadvantage) factors within a proposal or problem, or the forces

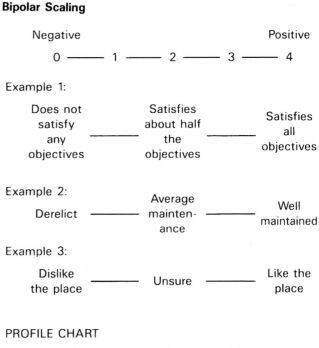

Bipolar Scaling

Negative   Positive

0 —— 1 —— 2 —— 3 —— 4

Example 1:

| Does not satisfy any objectives | —— | Satisfies about half the objectives | —— | Satisfies all objectives |

Example 2:

| Derelict | —— | Average maintenance | —— | Well maintained |

Example 3:

| Dislike the place | —— | Unsure | —— | Like the place |

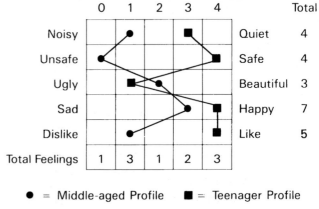

PROFILE CHART

	0	1	2	3	4		Total
Noisy		●		■		Quiet	4
Unsafe	●				■	Safe	4
Ugly		■	●			Beautiful	3
Sad				●	■	Happy	7
Dislike		●		■		Like	5
Total Feelings	1	3	1	2	3		

● = Middle-aged Profile   ■ = Teenager Profile

Figure 9.4

Proposal to build a power station

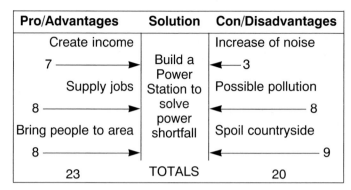

Pro/Advantages	Solution	Con/Disadvantages
Create income 7 ——————▶	Build a Power Station to solve power shortfall	Increase of noise ◀—— 3
Supply jobs 8 ——————▶		Possible pollution ◀—————— 8
Bring people to area 8 ——————▶		Spoil countryside ◀—————— 9
23	TOTALS	20

Figure 9.5 Force Field Scaling: Solution Focus

acting to produce a current problem and those forces working against a solution. Each set of opposing forces is drawn in a simple diagram to represent the dynamics of the decision-making problem.

It is a useful visual representation of good and bad features, or factors working in each direction on the problem you are trying to solve. The method concentrates on balancing and comparing elements inside a decision problem. Two examples are given, each with a different focus:

- a *solution focus* for a power station in a countryside area of some beauty, to solve an energy shortfall problem (Figure 9.5)

- a *problem focus* situation involving pedestrian/traffic conflict in a town centre (Figure 9.6).

1 Describe, in simple words, a proposed solution (Figure 9.5) or the current problem situation (Figure 9.6). Put that at the centre of your forcefield diagram.

2 When the focus, as in Figure 9.6, is on a *current problem situation* that you need to solve:

   a) describe a proposed solution and draw this on one side of the diagram.
   b) describe the main factor that is creating the current problem and draw it on the other side.

3 Write down two lists:

   - For Figure 9.5, where the focus is on a *solution*:

     a) draw the pro/advantage factors on one side.
     b) draw the con/disadvantage factors on the other side.

   - For Figure 9.6, where the focus is a *current problem* situation:

     a) draw the factors that are creating or reinforcing the current problem on the side for 'creating the problem'.
     b) draw the factors that are preventing your solution on the side with the 'solution'.

4 Draw arrows to the centre under each factor to show the conflicts (each entry need not be partnered by a similar one on the other side) between pro/con or creating/solving.

5 Scale each of the factors 1–10, with 10 being a strong factor. Write this figure on the line and vary the length of the line accordingly, to give you a quick visual impression of the weight of each factor.

6 *Summing the scores* can show the balance of forces, and the arrows will give a *visual impression*.

Traffic–Pedestrian Conflict

Creating the Problem			Solving the Problem	
Problem Creators?	**What is Reinforcing This?**	**Current Problem**	**Barriers to the Solution**	**Solutions?**
Too many vehicles	High car ownership 3 ——▶ More shops being built 6 ——————▶ Lack of alternative through routes 9 ——————▶	Traffic/ pedestrian conflict in town centre	Lack of finance ◀—————— 8 Local resident opposition ◀—— 5 Government funding reductions ◀—————— 9	Build a by-pass
	18	TOTALS	22	

Figure 9.6 Forcefield Scaling: Problem Focus

7 We might also look closer at the totals:

   a) in Figure 9.5, concentrating on the advantages as they appear stronger and thus easier to reinforce

   b) in Figure 9.6, concentrating on removing the barriers to our solution, rather than reducing the factors that are creating the problem

8 We can also consider the individual factors or arguments in both examples:

   a) make other decisions in order to add to, or strengthen the positive factors, or, eliminate or reduce the negative factors.

   b) concentrate on the factors we have rated highest, as they are likely to give the quickest returns.

G QUID Scaling

QUID is an acronym for 'QUantified Individual Decision-making', and this simple rated checklist summing method focuses on your individual or personal decision making. It is most useful when you have to evaluate a particular solution, or decide whether or not to adopt a particular specific proposal (it therefore differs from forcefield scaling, which concentrates on the balances between factors affecting a proposal).

1 Define the precise solution you want to evaluate. This is the most important stage: make it simple and limited and let it suggest the alternatives, for and against. Put it at the top of the page (Figure 9.7).

2 Add a list giving the arguments in favour of the solution.

3 Add a second list of all the arguments against the solution.

4 Assign weights to each of the arguments or factors you have listed. Ten points for those rated extremely important, down to one point for factors only of minor influence or importance.

5 Work out the raw total for each set of arguments or factors (this is the *total strength of all the arguments*).

6 Work out the mean for each set of arguments or factors (this is the *average strength of the arguments*).

7 If the difference in raw totals or means is less than 1, then the balance is so close that you will need to include more factors or more information.

8 If the difference is more than 1, then a decision is made on the highest raw total or mean side. If it

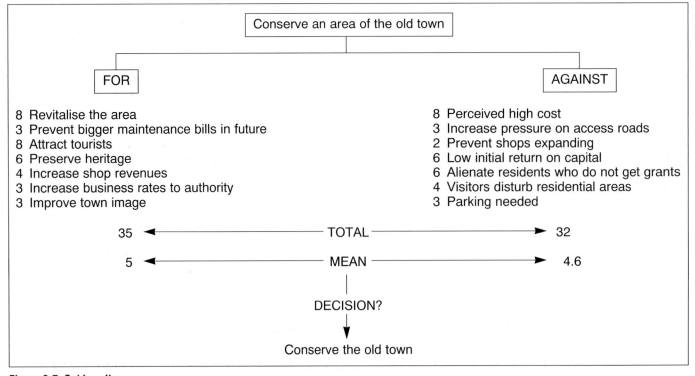

Figure 9.7 Quid scaling

much more than 1, then the decision you should make is even more obvious.

9 If the differences between the raw total scores and between the mean scores both point in the same direction, then you are in a strong position to make a clear decision. If, however, they point in different directions, then you may need to reduce the number of factors and concentrate on the more important, higher weighted ones.

Watchpoints on Scaling

1 Scaling attempts to apportion relative weights or position to data and thereby allow analysis, it is therefore subjective, individual to you and open to bias. As scaling is personal, be very careful not to read too much spurious exactness from the figures themselves – they are only a guess!

2 Scaling uses ranking and rating, and all detailed results are dependent on the level of measure used, whether nominal, ordinal, weighted or probability.

3 Scaling is used in many other techniques, often as an important early step to deeper analysis.

4 It can be particularly useful where qualitative data is used, or when dealing with geographical human behavioural problems.

5 Scaling can become far more accurate with practice, since your ability to rank and rate will improve.

6 Scaling must be seen to be a subjective measure or tentative indication and all figures derived from it should be seen in this light, not as definite or absolute quantities. Therefore, *never* be tempted to undertake sophisticated statistical tests on subjective scaling.

7 The method may lead you to rank and rate just about everything, because, somehow, the fact that there is now a figure attached to an idea is more comforting or it 'looks more scientific'. Resist the temptation!

10 | *The Matrix*

A matrix is a diagram of two or more dimensions drawn to highlight the relationships between the dimensions. It is one of the most adaptable and useful techniques which can help the decision-maker at all stages of the decision process, whenever there is a need to bring order to the data, compare information, rank or rate data, summarize findings, compute pay-offs or evaluate alternative possibilities.

Once constructed in a matrix, whether you have numerical or qualitative data, simple row and column counts can add immeasurably to your understanding of your data and your decision process. A matrix is simple and neat and allows you to look closely at variables and their relationships.

A The Rectangular Matrix

A two-dimensional grid of rectangular shape. The rows represent one set of data, the columns the other set and the intersecting cells show the relationship between the individual variables in each set, at that point (Figure 10.1).

1 **Cross-tabulation** In the example, field data on journeys to work between three cities is recast into a rectangular matrix. This highlights the relationships between the cities and allows row and column totals to be easily calculated, so giving the decision-maker much more useful summary information (Figure 10.2). Cross-tabulations are also a good way to check for errors or omissions in your data.

2 **Checklist matrix** A simple indexed matrix, sometimes called a *placement matrix*, can provide a useful summary of information, by plotting the relationship against two axes. No attempt is made in this simple form to quantify the cell entries. In this example, four sites are compared on existing facilities, enabling gaps to be identified and opportunities realized (Figure 10.3).

3 **Summary matrix** The matrix is a useful 'housekeeping' device to store data and provide summary or précis information; it does not have to be used simply with numerical information. The example shows a summary of interest groups' ideas on a new town plan (Figure 10.4).

Cross Tabulation

Field Data: Journey to Work

From City	To City	Number of Journeys
1	1	10
1	2	20
1	3	30
2	1	20
2	2	25
2	3	40
3	1	5
3	2	30
3	3	50

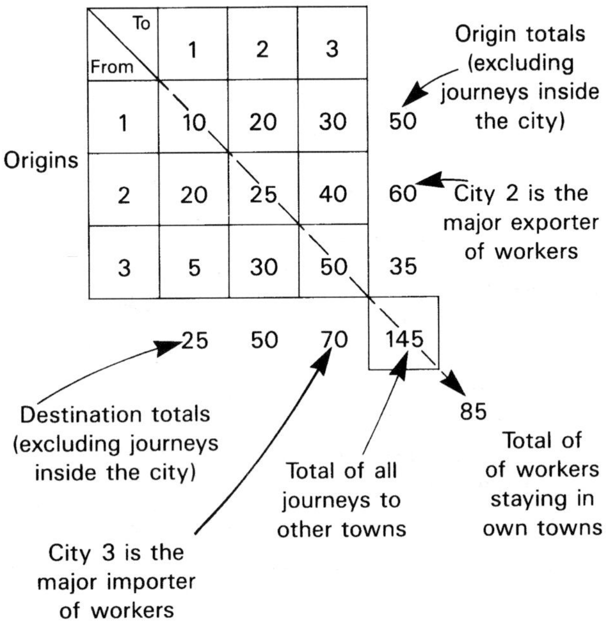

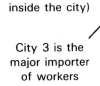

OVERALL:

City 1 = 50 − 25 = Net 25 Journeys Out

City 2 = 60 − 50 = Net 10 Journeys Out

City 3 = 70 − 35 = Net 35 Journeys In, and
the highest number of workers staying in
the city (50). It would appear then to be
the most important in the supply of jobs.

145 + 85 = 230 workers in the region travel to
work, or were surveyed

Figure 10.2

The Rectangular Matrix

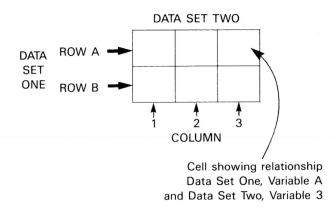

Cell showing relationship
Data Set One, Variable A
and Data Set Two, Variable 3

Figure 10.1

Checklist Matrix

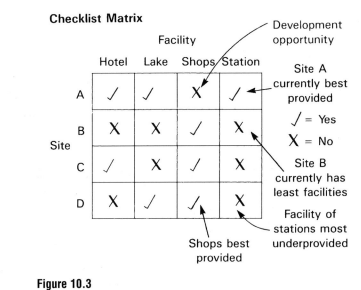

Figure 10.3

Summary Matrix

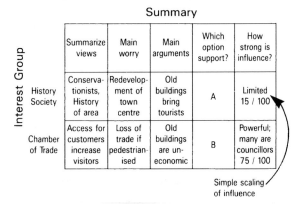

Figure 10.4

Compatibility / Conflict Matrix

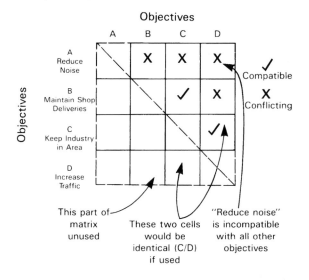

Figure 10.5

Evaluation Matrices

SIMPLE MATRIX

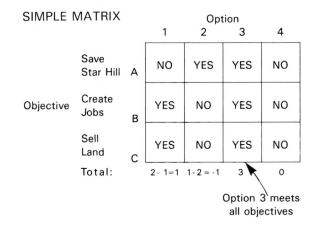

Option 3 meets all objectives

Figure 10.6i

SCALED MATRIX

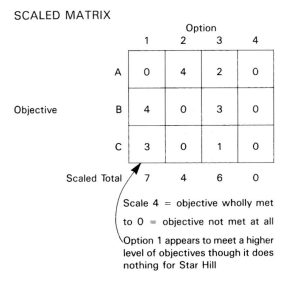

Scale 4 = objective wholly met
to 0 = objective not met at all

Option 1 appears to meet a higher level of objectives though it does nothing for Star Hill

Figure 10.6ii

WEIGHTED MATRIX

	Option			
	1	2	3	4
A	0	4X3	2X3	0
Objective B	4X2	0	3X2	0
C	3X1	0	1X1	0
Weighted Total	11	12	13	0

Option 3 meets all objectives in part and more of the important ones

Weighting: Objective A = 3 (highest priority)
B = 2
C = 1 (lowest priority)

Figure 10.6iii

Precedence Matrix

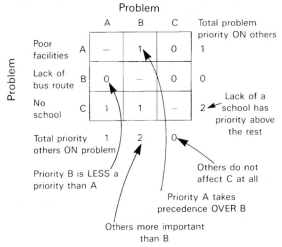

Figure 10.7

Pay-off Matrix

	Event		Total Utility
	Sunny	Raining	
Stay in bed	Poor — miss nice weather. Utility = 30	Not bad — save a soaking but miss walk. Utility = 50	30 + 50 = 80
Go for walk	Ideal! best combination. Utility = 100	Poor — get soaked! Utility = 10	100 + 10 = 110

Options

Outcome cell

Best outcome   Worst outcome

Figure 10.8

4 Compatibility/conflict matrix The dimensions, or axes, of the matrix can also be identical, to allow the relationships *within one set of data* to be compared. The example shows a set of project objectives cross-referenced against each other. Note that it is not necessary to complete the whole matrix, since the two halves on each side of the diagonal are identical. Here, it would not be possible to reduce noise *and* solve the other problems (Figure 10.5).

5 Evaluation matrix The matrix provides a neat and quick method for evaluation of options in decision-making. Simple Yes/No answers to the meeting of objectives by options can be scaled as Yes = 1, No = 0 and summed for comparison (Figure 10.6i). A *scaled or ranked matrix*, with the extent of meeting of objectives included, can provide different answers, if the information allows such refinement (10.6ii). A *weighted matrix* adds even further information, where it is possible to rank and rate the importance of the objectives themselves (10.6iii).

6 Precedence matrix The priority order of options, objectives or problems, can be created with a precedence matrix, which records simple entries of 1 or 0. This can be useful, as it might show you which action to take first, or which elements are most important and therefore should be funded and which elements are less important to the success of your decision. *Rows* score priority of the row variable on or over the others; *columns* score the priority of other variables on or over the column variable. A score of 1 represents higher priority, 0 a lower priority. Study of the example (Figure 10.7) will make the method clearer, a useful technique to identify key problems and relative importance of issues.

7 Pay-off matrix A useful summary of the outcomes of decision options under different chance event conditions. By adding utility scaling, the totals can be used to decide on a strategy (Figure 10.8). With uncertain weather, should you stay in bed or go for a walk? What you decide to do depends on your personality and objectives: if you are an optimist and gambler you will take a MAXIMAX view and opt for the best overall pay-off which will include the best outcome (utility = 110): you would go for a walk and chance the rain. If, on the other hand, you are a pessimist, you might take a MAXIMIN approach and opt for the option giving the least-worst outcome. If you go for a walk and it rains, your utility is the worst possible (10), so as a good pessimist, stay in bed and your lowest utility is as high as 30!

8 Failure matrix Sometimes it is useful to look at the failures or adverse consequences that may arise if you do NOT take a particular decision, or to identify what might go wrong with a decision after it is implemented. You can then include in your decision report, actions which might remove or reduce the chance of those adverse effects occurring.

a Identify the vulnerable areas in your decision – what could go wrong? (Figure 10.9)
b Construct a matrix with five columns, with the headings:

- Possible failure
- Likelihood or probability of that failure occurring (rate 1 to 10, with 10 highest)
- Seriousness or impact of this failure on the decision taken (rate 1 to 10)
- Rate, by multiplying likelihood with seriousness

Building a groyne to stop beach drift

Possible failure	Likelihood or probability of occurring (A)	Seriousness or impact if occurs (B)	Rate (A×B)	Rank
Major storm destroys groyne	1	10	10	4
Construction firm goes bankrupt	2	6	12	3
Council runs out of funds to promote new beach to tourists	7	3	21	1
Groyne fails to stabilize beach	3	5	15	2

Figure 10.9 Failure Matrix

3-Dimensional Matrix

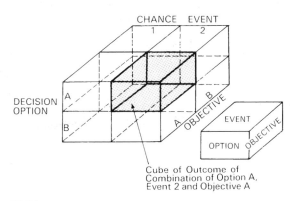

Figure 10.10

- Rank from 1, the most probable and serious failure, downwards

c Identify the highest ranked, and therefore most important, of the possible consequential failures in your decision plan and work out and add actions to reduce or eliminate them.

The example is for a plan to build a groyne on a beach to stop longshore drift and to stabilize the foreshore to help to attract tourists into a holiday resort. The decision to build has been made; now what could go wrong and how could we soften the effects of the most problematical failures? In terms of probability, the council's promotion of the new beach is the most likely to present us with problems. In terms of seriousness, a major storm would be worst failure, but it is the most unlikely to occur. On balance then, we need to address ways to overcome the problem of promoting the newly stabilized beach to the tourists if our plan is to succeed.

9 **Presentation matrix** Matrices can also be used to summarize, store and present detailed information – the cells do not have to contain only one set of information, as in the summary matrix. For example, a matrix with axes listing countries against GNP could simply have the relevant GNP figures in each cell, or it might also include a breakdown of each individual GNP into industrial categories, together with an indication of the level of change since a previous year and even a prediction of future movements in the index. Some of the entries may be figures, yet others may be words, symbols or graphics.

The presentation matrix can be particularly useful to give detailed evidence to justify your arguments for a particular decision in your final report.

B The Three-Dimensional Matrix

This is a method to cross-relate three dimensions of the information (Figure 10.10) but it can appear complex and is not recommended for normal use.

C The Concentric Circle Matrix

This is a way to prompt a decision-maker to look at all the combinations of variables involved in complex problems.

1 Identify the decisions, events or objectives (the variables).

2 List the options or possibilities for each.

3 Draw a matrix of these as concentric circles, with the one with fewer options at the centre (Figure 10.11).

4 Cut carefully around each circle, then reassemble and rotate each in turn, so bringing each of all the possible combinations out in turn.

The Concentric Circle Matrix

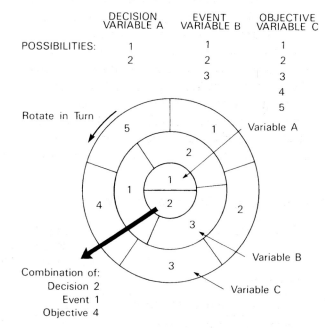

Figure 10.11

Watchpoints on Matrices

1 A really flexible friend to the decision-maker, it can be used at all stages of the decision process and is extremely adaptable – it is one of the jewels in your crown!

2 An essential aid, as it brings clarity to your sorting of data and so aids your decision-making.

3 The visual result from constructing a matrix can reveal relationships in your data that you might not otherwise notice.

4 Remember that any matrix having exactly the same factors along both axes will have either a mirror-image effect in the two halves, separated by the diagonal, or will use only one half of the matrix. A good example of the latter is the 'distance between cities' matrix found often in atlases – it uses the names of the cities on both axes so that reading the cell where they intersect gives you the appropriate distance. Note that the example cross-tabulation matrix (Figure 10.2) does have cities on both axes, but they are not the same, since one axis gives cities as destinations, the other as origins.

5 Enable large data sets to be summarized, compared and analysed as single units, but be careful not to make them too complex.

6 Can be used with figures, ranks, words and graphics; it should not be seen as simply a mathematical aid. It can use qualitative and symbolic as well as quantitative data.

7 Annotate matrices – it helps to highlight the main points and may prevent you forgetting an important relationship you have seen.

8 Statistical significance tests, Pearson Rank Correlation or Chi-Squared, can easily be computed from a matrix in order to analyse your data further.

9 Always put entries that you want to compare in the *columns* of a matrix, not the rows, as we all find it easier to compare horizontally.

11 *Classification*

Classification is the amalgamating of variables into groups or categories of like variables in order to identify patterns in the information, isolate a smaller number of categories for mapping and analysis, and generally to make the information clearer and simpler to work with by collating or storing it in a convenient form.

Classification is an essential early step to organising your data. Most often, data on its own is comparatively meaningless and useless – only when classified and grouped can it begin to make sense, and only then can comparisons be made with the rest of the information. If data cannot be used because it is not classified, or inappropriately grouped, then it can hardly be used for deeper analysis or decision-making. There are many techniques to subdivide data into classes or groups and the appropriate method will depend on the data to be used:

• *Numerically-based or quantitative data* can use quartiles, equal spacing or some statistical measure: even just the mean or a percentage reworking of the information may tell you a great deal. With this kind of data the table, matrix and scattergraph can also be useful.

• *Literal (in words) or qualitative data* is more difficult to classify and involves you in searching harder for obvious criteria to use to break down the information into meaningful classes. A matrix is useful for such data, and charts for presentation.

The aim of classification is to provide an identity for data, to reduce information to manageable and meaningful classes, to organize your information so that you understand it and, ultimately, arrive at a decision. It is important, then, to take a logical and common-sense approach from the start.

Method

1 Identify the kinds of information you are using, and the units of measurement.

2 Try to see if there are any obvious, or useful, factors that seem to occur in most of the data, which might be used to split it up into manageable elements.

3 Use a general principle that data bearing a clearly identified relationship with one another should be classified together, or at least placed in nearby groups.

4 Look ahead to your analysis of the data and assess what categories would be most useful at that stage. Are there any important elements you really must include and which might be the basis of categorizing?

5 Are you going to use all of the data you have, as it is presented, or would it be better to amalgamate or combine some of the information?

6 Group your information using a simple method of presentation, to save time, perhaps a matrix, a table, Venn diagram or even just a listed index. These methods can be a means of classifying your data, as you choose the elements to include.

Example:

Sets are collections of distinguishably similar objects and *Venn diagrams* are visual impressions of the number of sets and their relationships. Figure 11.1 shows two features mapped, categorized in a Venn diagram and the number of categories listed. Note that the number of categories is dependent on the combinations you wish to allow (no more than four in a Venn diagram), and the choice of combinations depends on your ability to see the most useful groups or parameters to define groups. In turn, this depends on the nature of the decision problem you are tackling.

Watchpoints on Classification

1 Many useful methods exist to collapse data into fewer, larger and more manageable groups, but many depend heavily on your ability to identify the key factors that can be used to split up and group the information.

2 A simple list or index of the information is a useful first step to understanding it – just produce a checklist and then try to find some logical order or sub-categories in the data.

3 Classification is a method of refining information to make it easier to use, and depends closely on the kind of data to be classified, and the units and scale of measurement used:

- *Quantitative* – usually easier to classify, uses figures and therefore tables or matrices may be appropriate to help classification.
- *Qualitative* – views or perceptions, which need to be scaled and organized carefully if you are to make sense of them.
- *Temporal* – depending on time periods or dates, again tables may help to order the information as it comes in a predefined sequence.
- *Spatial* – classified on location in space, distance from a point or some other spatial measure. Here some means of grouping on a map may be most useful, either by eye or by specific measurement.

4 Once classified, you can use other methods to analyse what you have found. So, always think ahead and classify to help the later stages of your work.

5 Within data sets there are often a number of dimensions that could be the basis of your classification – for example, do you use time periods or groupings of like settlements, or geographical regions to classify census population data? Think about which is most appropriate to reaching your decision.

6 There is always more than one method of classifying information – you have to choose that which is most appropriate, logical and useful to your argument and your problem.

Sets and Venn Diagram

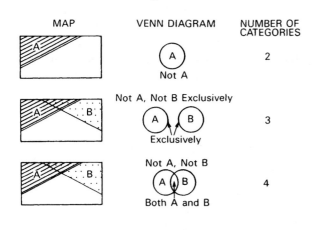

Figure 11.1

12 Charting

Charts, graphs or diagrams are quickly produced, useful visual representations of information to highlight *relationships in your data*: the overall structure, composition, trend or character of your information. They can be of use in classifying and analysing data, in identifying patterns, in illustrating reports and in presenting final decisions. They are particularly useful when comparing data sets to show relationships over time periods, to reveal unexpected associations and to make complex situations easier to understand.

Charts should be:

• clear

• understandable

• relevant

• concise

• as simple as possible

• able to convey a message

Method

A Arithmetical Line Graph

Arithmetical scales are where equal divisions on the scale represent *equal quantities*, so, one division is always 10, or 100, or whatever, without variation.

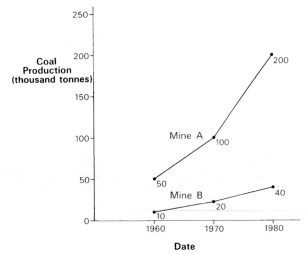

Arithmetical Line Graph

Figure 12.1

1 Draw and annotate both axes, usually the independent variable on the horizontal or x axis (e.g. time periods) and the dependent variable on the vertical or y axis (decide which variable is which by considering which one makes the other change).

2 Ensure that you can accommodate the range of your data.

3 Select the proportions of your chart so that it, and any annotation or text, will fit on the page.

4 Plot the data sets, using different point symbols if you are using a number of sets.

5 Draw appropriate lines between the data points.

6 Add annotation, key, scales, title and unit measurements.

7 It is possible to show multiple data sets by using two vertical axes if you are comparing two data sets, for example. A common example is temperatures in a line graph and precipitation by histogram on a single chart. Here, one vertical axis would have temperature degrees, the other millimetres of precipitation – the scales would be different and so difficult to compare exactly, but they could give a good visual impression of when it might be best to take your holiday in a particular place.

This is a quick and easy method to draw to show *absolute changes in data* – in Figure 12.1, Mine A appears to have greater production that is increasing more rapidly than Mine B. Note that we draw *straight lines* between the points because the data points are discrete variables, (e.g. counts of customers in a supermarket or production figures) and so the intervening points have no significance (we cannot tell what production was at any point between the audit dates of 1960, 1970 and 1980).

We only draw *smooth curves* between points if the data points are in a continuous series (e.g. temperatures), because then all intervening points do have significance and we can estimate what those intervening points will be.

We can also use more complex arithmetical line charts:

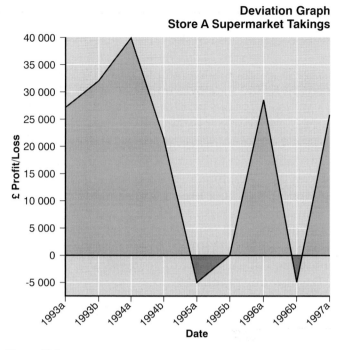

Figure 12.2

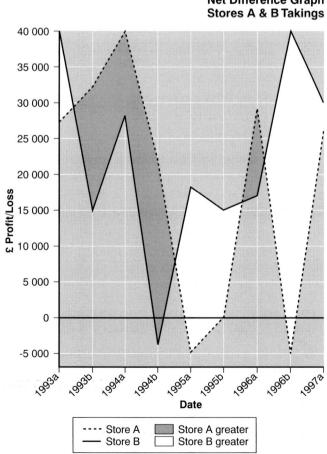

Figure 12.3

Deviation Graph This is used to show changes over time and the range of change on either side of a constant (usually zero). Figure 12.2 shows the profits and losses of a supermarket over time.

Net Difference Graph This takes the Deviation Graph further to show *two sets of data*. The area between the lines, and the individual distances between the related points at each time period, show the variable differences between the data sets over time. In the example (Figure 12.3), we have added the turnover of another supermarket and can now compare turnover between the two. We can see when they appear to have similar results, when they diverged and which, when and by how much, either was ahead of the other. This might help us to explain what was happening and lead us to investigate further.

Accumulated Area Graph If you have, for example, four data sets of occupational categories over time (Figure 12.4), an accumulated area graph can illustrate the relative size or importance of each over time, in a way that separate, individual graphs would not.

1 Plot the absolute points for Category One up from the base.

2 Plot Category Two by measuring up from the points plotted for Category One, not from the baseline.

3 Continue to the end.

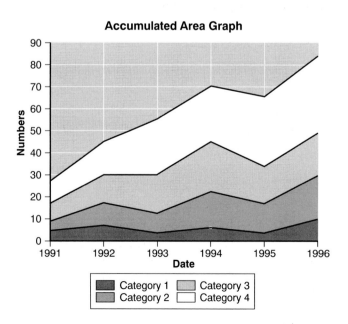

Figure 12.4

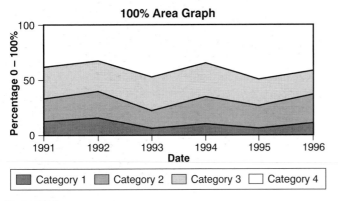

Figure 12.5

The relative height of each Category at each year can be easily compared, and the areas covered by each category's shading show the absolute relative changes over the period in a visual way.

100% Area Graphs These data sets, if converted into percentages of the whole, can be plotted. But this time, the top of the graph represents 100% of the whole and we can see, through time, what proportion of the whole was taken up by each occupational category (Figure 12.5). Again, the *areas* represented by the categories give a measure of the proportionate importance of each over the whole time period.

These arithmetical line graphs are useful, but many people find the more involved ones difficult to interpret because the baseline for each data set is different.

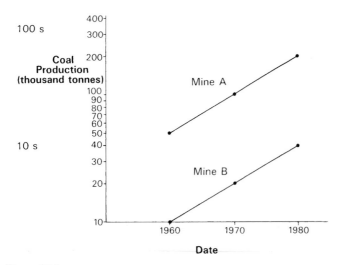

Figure 12.6

B Logarithmic Line Graph

Logarithmic scales are such that equal divisions on the scale represent *equal divisions of rate, or factors of change* in the data, for example, 0.01, 0.1, 1, 10, 100, 1000 (Figure 12.6), where intervals on the log scale are all exponents of 10. These can be used with percentage change data or raw values and we usually use 'semi-logarithmic' paper, which has a logarithmic scale only on the vertical axis, so that we can plot, say, time periods on an arithmetic horizontal scale (our example is semi-logarithmic).

The data from Figure 12.1, when plotted on logarithmic graph paper, yields straight lines for both mines, showing the *relative rate of change* in production at each mine to be identical.

Logarithmic graphs are:

• good for investigating rates or factors of change

• useful to accommodate wide ranges in data, by using the cycles of scales on the paper (so you need to choose the correct kind of log graph paper before you begin)

• good for showing relative, not absolute, change

• difficult to interpret because of the varying scale

• of no use if you need to show zero for your data, as the logarithm of zero cannot be defined and so the x axis always starts at 1 or 10 or another exponent of 10.

C Circular, Polar or Radial Graph

These graphs are for data presented with some *continuous, sequential or recurring* element that can be best shown as circular and they are useful for:

• *recurrent features* (e.g. trade figures or crop production by months of the year, where each time period would be 360° divided by 12 months = 30°)

• *continuous, sequential time periods* (such as sunshine over 24 hours, where each time period would be 360° divided by 24 hours = 15°)

• *directional features* (e.g. numbers of erratics by compass direction, or a wind rose showing the percentage of time or number of hours winds blew from different directions). These are usually referred to as *Radial Graphs*.

Circular, Polar or Radial Graph

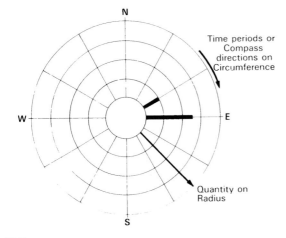

Figure 12.7

1 The two scales or dimensions are measured on the *circumference* and the *radius* of the circle (Figure 12.7). On the *circumference,* which is often time, zero or start the scale at the vertical from the centre point and work in a clockwise direction.

   On the *radius*, measure the scale from the centre outwards in concentric circles.

2 Points are plotted and, depending on the data, either joined with lines around the circle, or plotted as bars from the centre of the circle.

More than one series of information can be plotted, for example to show variations in daily farming activities during a year. In this case the areas between activity lines can be shaded to identify proportions of activity change throughout the year (Figure 12.8). Such a graph is sometimes called a *Sector Graph*.

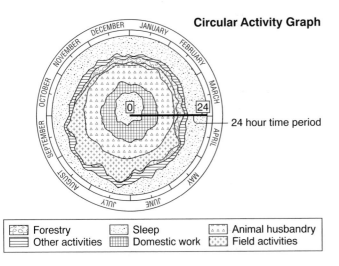

Circular Activity Graph

24 hour time period

| Forestry | Sleep | Animal husbandry |
| Other activities | Domestic work | Field activities |

Figure 12.8

Be wary of circular, polar or radial graphs, because:

• they can be difficult to interpret because the arrangement of axes is so unusual.

• they have a tendency to visually reduce the apparent range of variations in data.

• they can become complex.

• the circumferential scale must be continuous and contiguous, such as a repeating time series or contiguous compass directions.

D Triangular Graph

Sometimes called a *Ternary Diagram* (Figure 12.9), this is a very useful method to examine varying proportions of three related datasets.

1 Use triangular graph paper, where the three sides of the equilateral triangle are the scales for the three factors to be plotted.

2 Each side is scaled from 0% to 100% and each apex of the triangle has one 0% and one 100%.

3 The zero for each percentage scale is along a side, the 100% is at an apex.

4 The three variables must be in the form of percentages of the whole, so you may need to convert raw data. For example, the proportion of primary, secondary and tertiary employment in a country may be identified. All values must add up to 100%.

5 Plot the points – notice that each point itself represents all three proportions which, at that point, add up to a combined 100% of the whole.

6 Grouping of points in different parts of the diagram indicates varying mixes of the three variables and so can give a quick visual impression of any patterns that exist.

7 Points may be joined by lines, or areas of the diagram shaded to highlight the patterns.

Triangular graphs are useful to:

• Give a good, strong visual impression of the relationships between three sets of data

• Show relationships between sub-categories of data

• Highlight which elements are dominant over others within the whole study

Triangular Graph

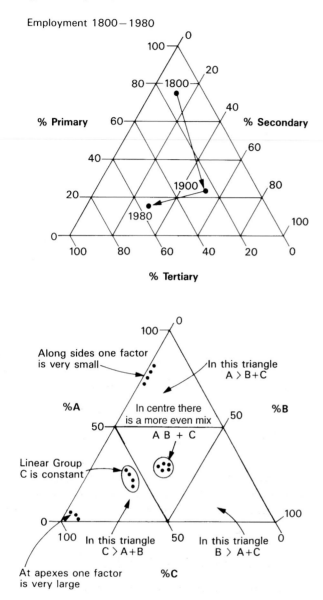

Figure 12.9

Scattergraph

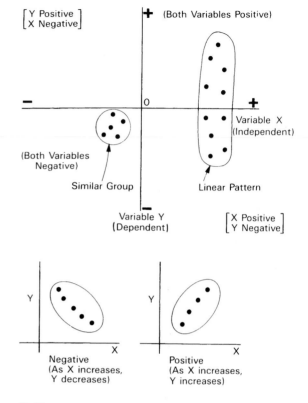

Figure 12.10

- Show changing poportions over time, as in the example, where we can see the movement of an economy from primary to tertiary activity dominance via secondary activity.

E Scattergraph

An extremely useful method for initial analysis of data to find patterns which might suggest further inquiry, by testing, graphically, whether two continuous variables are related. It is therefore very often used in the first stages of an investigation.

1 Use two intersecting axes, each with positive and negative ends, so creating four quadrants (Figure 12.10).

2 Plot data on the x and y co-ordinates, dependent data on the vertical axis, independent on the horizontal axis.

3 It sometimes helps to label points, either with different symbols, numbers or text labels. This makes the graph clearer to read, helps you to compose your explanation of the graph and identifies points that you may then refer to in your written report.

4 Depending on the data type, points can be: joined by lines by hand, joined by calculated lines (for example, calculated by regression), ringed by hand to identify groups or related points, or shaded by hand to show the groups you can identify.

5 The patterns of points show:

- Close patterns of dots which indicate similarity

- Lines of dots indicate some kind of consistent relationship
- negative if sloping down to the right in the north-east sector
- positive if sloping up to the right in the north-east sector
- Total scatter indicates lack of probable relationship.

6 The quadrants show:

- Anything in the north-east quadrant will be positive on both variables
- Anything in the south-west quadrant will be negative on both variables
- The other quadrants are positive on one and negative on the other variable.

Useful for:

a Quickly classifying data sets by identifying groupings and so targeting your investigations

b Showing the direction *and* strength of relationships between variables

c Identifying unusual points, or outliers, outside the general pattern of the points, which might affect means or other statistical measures disproportionately (or might just identify the most important points!)

d Indicating a pattern to be investigated by statistical or other measures.

e The scattergraph can use qualitative data, or the results from a questionnaire survey, as long as this data is ranked and rated (for example, you could plot age of respondent on one axis and results of a survey which could be rated, say, from quiet and withdrawn to dominant and aggressive on the other axis).

F Lorenz Curve

A graph to measure the extent to which variables are evenly distributed, or, more exactly, how far the distribution is equal or unequal. For example, we might plot the acreage of farms in different sizes in a State (Figure 12.11), or employment in industry in different cities. It works with *cumulative frequencies* on a graph where both axes have scales of 100%, so that the points plotted are cumulative percentages of the total.

1 Draw up a suitably scaled graph, with 0% to 100% on each axis, and zero in the joining corner.

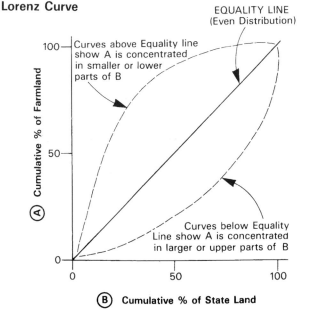

Lorenz Curve

Figure 12.11

2 Draw the 'equality line' from zero diagonally up to the point at which both variables are 100%.

3 Arrange variable data in order of size.

4 Work each out as a percentage of each distribution.

5 Add the percentages together as cumulative percentages, adding each to the ones preceding it.

6 Plot the points.

7 Join the points with straight lines.

8 Compare your line with the equality line.

- *Lines which follow the equality line* show equality (in the example diagram this would mean that farmland is equally distributed across the state), where there is a perfect match between the two lines.
- *Lines away from the equality line* show increasingly less equality of distribution or more deviation from equal distribution – so more localization or regional concentration of farmland in the example.

9 It is possible to plot a second line, for example, from data derived from your decision to change something in the problem, then compare the effects of your decision and your new line on the original line.

G Running Mean

If data fluctuates wildly on a graph, it can be difficult to see the underlying trend or pattern. The running mean (sometimes called the *moving average*) evens out the individual peaks and troughs to give a smoother mean line which summarizes the overall trend. In the example (Figure 12.12), 1970 was a good production year, but the running mean line shows an overall fall-off since 1940. Was 1970 an unusual, one-off peak?

1 Take individual data in groups of 3 (or any other odd number).

2 Add up the first three figures and find their mean. In our example, take 1900–1920, add them up (10 + 20 + 15 = 45) and find the mean (45 ÷ 3 = 15).

3 Give that value to the middle year of the group (1910). The distribution will then be *centred* (if we had taken an even number of years to calculate we would have had to either plot the mean between two years, or average adjacent years, so we tend to use odd numbers of years as groups).

4 Do the same for each successive, *overlapping* group (the next group of three in the example is thus 1910–1930, and their mean would be plotted for 1920).

5 Plot the summary line and compare with the original.

6 If the line still shows great variation, try calculating a five-year moving average, and so on.

7 If we are using a three-year trend then we cannot plot averages for the first and last years (1900 and 1980 in our example).

H Bar Chart

Bar charts show (Figure 12.13) by the length *or* height of simple bars or columns against a scale (See *histogram*), a visual overview of the distribution of *categorical data*, and are thus most often used for initial analysis of information, to identify relative frequencies of data and to show the most frequent factor.

1 Draw up a suitably scaled graph with *categories* on the horizontal axis and *frequencies* on the vertical axis.

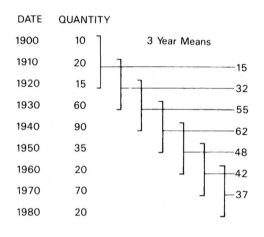

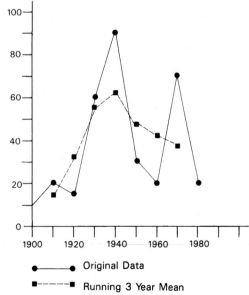

Figure 12.12

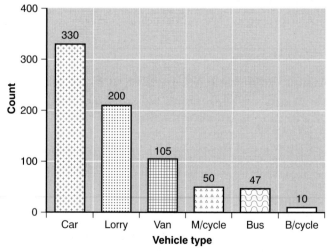

Figure 12.13

2 Plot values as bars, with spaces between each bar and bars of equal width, where the height *or* length of the bar is proportionate to its value (they are therefore different to histograms, where the *area* of the bars is used).

3 Sometimes it is easier (for example, if all values apply to a single time period) to plot horizontal rather than vertical bars, in which case, simply swap the scales. It all depends on what you see as clearest.

4 Draw the bars with the largest at the left or bottom and the others in rank order of size, or according to a logical ordering of the data.

5 Annotate each bar so that it is clear what it represents.

Pros:

• they are so commonly used and very versatile

• easy to understand and to construct

• good to show relative sizes of variables and magnitudes of measurements in simple categorized data

• good to show changes over time

• divided or segmented bars, where each bar is itself sub-divided to show its components, are also commonly used (in our example we might subdivide each bar by the age or year code of the vehicle registration numbers)

• they can be used, by having a scale which crosses above and below a zero line, to show positive and negative values

• it is possible to use three-dimensional or even pictorial bars

• the common *population pyramid* chart is a form of divided bar graph, used to show the age and sex structure of populations.

Cons:

• can be confusing if more than one scale is used

• subdividing bars must be done with extreme caution as the results are difficult to compare visually

• do not include too many bars

• always have a very clear scale on the graph

• because they are so versatile, there is a tendency to make them too complex, remember that *clarity* is our goal

I Histogram

Histograms also use bars to show variables, but here it is the *area* of the bars, not their length or height (as with *Bar Charts*), which show the value of the entry. They are mostly used to analyse the distribution of values for continuous data, measured within a range of possible values (for example, temperatures, time periods, salary levels or distances from a central point), usually by using some kind of measuring device. They are used to identify distributions within classes and, as they use rectangles and the areas within rectangles to show the distribution of their data, they can be seen as stepped graphs.

1 Draw a graph of suitable dimensions with the feature whose *size* is being analysed on the horizontal axis, and the *frequency* of occurrence on the vertical axis.

2 Plot the information as contiguous rectangular columns (any gaps between columns would show a zero frequency for a class at that point).

3 Use appropriate class intervals on the horizontal scale (Figure 12.14). Either divide the range of the data into the number of classes you need, with each class of equal magnitude; or select more commonly used classes, for example, young, middle and older age categories; or use a scatter graph to suggest natural breaks in the data.

4 It is common to vary the width, and hence the area of the columns, if the classes used for the x axis are of dissimilar magnitudes. In Figure 12.14, the bars for salary categories £20,000–£29,999 and £30,000–£40,000 are twice as wide as the others because their range is twice that of the lower salary groups.

5 To be accurate, frequencies should be plotted in proportion to the area of the bar, so the height is of secondary value in assessing frequencies:

• If you double the interval width of the base of the columns, in general, you halve the height.

• Normally, we start from the smallest figure and scale the other columns accordingly.

Be careful to distinguish between bar charts and histograms:

• Histograms are frequently confused with the simpler bar charts, indeed, bar charts are often wrongly called histograms.

**Histogram
Salary Distribution**

Key	£ Salary Range	Frequency	Block width	Scaling factor	Block height
A	0–4,999	4	2	1	4
B	5,000–9,999	4	2	1	4
C	10,000–14,999	6	2	1	6
D	15,000–19,999	8	2	1	8
E	20,000–29,999	10	4	0.5	5
F	30,000–40,000	6	4	0.5	3

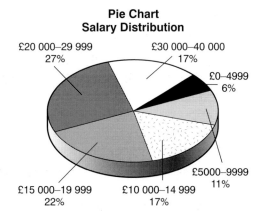

Figure 12.14

- Histograms are more difficult to do and can use *continuous data*; bar charts use *categorical data*.

- Remember that histograms essentially record *the distribution of measurements* and that it is their *area* that is important.

- With histograms, the bars are drawn contiguous, touching, because they are recording frequencies along a *continuous scale*.

- Strictly, the 'bars' of a histogram are rectangles with:

    - the *base of the rectangle* representing the class intervals, which may not be all of equal size
    - the *area of the rectangle* representing the number of measurements in that particular class
    - therefore, we have to be careful when reading off from the *vertical scale* as it can be confusing until you are familiar with the proper nature of histograms.

J Boxplot

A simple graphical, visual method for identifying the main summary patterns in your data.

1 Draw an appropriately scaled graph with *items measured, or classes*, on the horizontal scale, and *values or frequencies* on the vertical scale.

2 Calculate for each class its median; its 25th and 75th percentiles; its highest and lowest values.

3 Plot the median as a short thick horizontal line.

4 Plot the 25th percentile and the 75th percentile as short horizontal lines.

5 Draw a box between the two percentiles and shade it in.

6 Plot the largest value and the smallest values as short horizontal lines.

7 Draw a vertical line between these two lines to

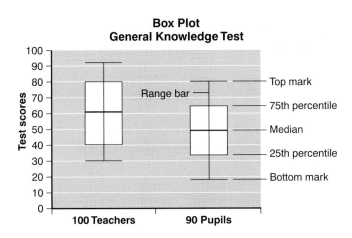

Figure 12.15

make a range bar (this is the range of your values).

8 Mark precisely any unusual values (e.g. a top or bottom mark way out of line with the rest).

9 Analyse the visual result.

Boxplots are good for:

- quick visual overviews of data spread and main summary statistical features

- identifying aberrant or unusual values

- pointing the way to better decisions, by focusing on basic patterns in the data set

- providing ideas to work on, or rapid comparisons of data sets.

Figure 12.15 shows the scores for teachers and pupils on a general knowledge test. The median for the teachers is higher, but the percentiles are wider apart (the box is bigger), showing much greater variability than the pupils. If other boxes had been plotted alongside we could compare more easily quite comprehensive sets of data – as the boxplot is a visual method, it is often more useful than relying solely on the calculated statistics from which it is derived.

K Pie Chart

These are graphs (sometimes called *divided circles*) which are drawn as circles and subdivided according to the percentage proportions of their constituent parts: each 'slice of the pie' is calculated as a number of degrees of the circle, according to its proportion of the whole. They are therefore used to illustrate how a whole is divided into its parts, and the percentage size of each of the parts.

1 Draw a circle of appropriate size.

2 Use *one* of these two methods next. *Either* calculate the percentages of the whole total represented by each of the variables (make sure they all add up to 100%). Then multiply each of the individual percentages by 3.6 to convert it to degrees (because the total for the circle is 360°, so each 1% is 3.6°). *Or* calculate the angles of each segment by using the formula:

$$\frac{vi}{total} \times 360$$

Where *vi* is the raw (not percentage) value of the individual component, *total* is the grand total value of all elements and 360 is the number of degrees in the circle. The result is the number of degrees for the individual element.

3 Add up all the individual degree calculations to make sure they total 360.

4 Draw the slices inside the circle, starting at the vertical and running clockwise, usually with the largest slice first.

5 Shade each slice.

6 Annotate to make clear:

- what each slice is showing (this is in addition to a key)
- the value of the slice (the raw value, not the percentage)
- annotate outside, not inside, the circle.

Things to look out for with *Pie Charts*:

- Do not include too many slices as it becomes too confusing – about 6 is ideal.

- No slice should be less than about 5° or 6°, otherwise it would be difficult to see.

- You may need to group variables together if too many are too small. This is not so effective if a number of values are very similar.

- You may be tempted to draw a number of pie charts to compare with each other – avoid doing this as they are notoriously difficult to read on their own, even without companions! However, this is commonly found in textbooks and on maps.

- They are good visually, as their individual elements are in area proportion to their percentage of the whole.

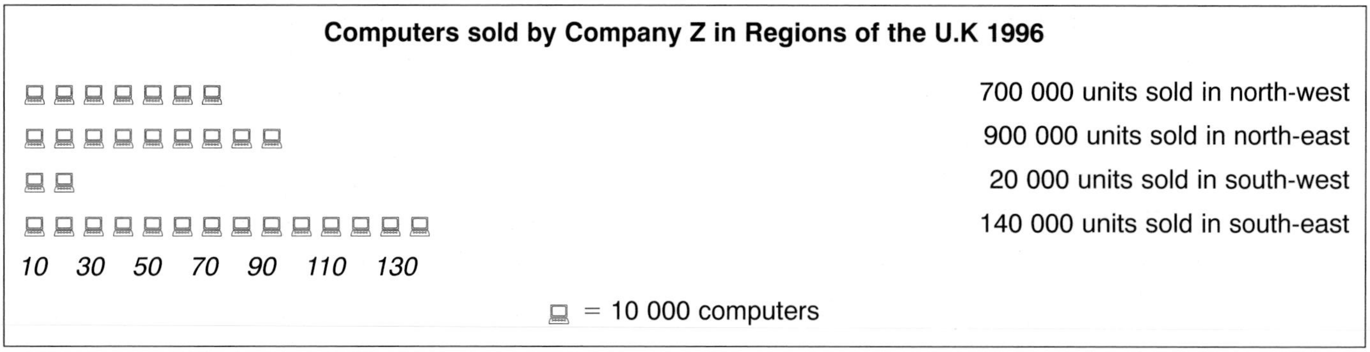

Computers sold by Company Z in Regions of the U.K 1996

700 000 units sold in north-west

900 000 units sold in north-east

20 000 units sold in south-west

140 000 units sold in south-east

10   30   50   70   90   110   130

💻 = 10 000 computers

Figure 12.16

- Make sure your methods of shading are distinct and cannot be confused with each other.

- Many software programs will draw pie charts for you – even in 3-D or with particular segments 'lifted out' of the pie to emphasise them. By all means use them, but always be careful to abide by the rule: keep it simple!

- Ensure that all labelling of slices is printed horizontally – you do not want to add even more confusion.

L Isotype or Pictographs

This is a form of bar graph that uses symbols, pictures or representations of the features it is presenting in rows or columns – silhouettes of soldiers for the armed forces, pound signs for money measures, sheafs of corn for grain yields or pictures of computers for figures relating to computing (Figure 12.16).

They are useful if:

- you want to produce a visually forceful chart – pictures have power, and simplified pictures are more memorable than lists of detailed figures!

- you want to produce a simple chart which is virtually self-explanatory

- to show comparisons – single items are not effectively shown this way

- you want to make your data appear more human and more interesting.

1 Calculate the bar lengths as in Section H above.

2 Choose symbols carefully to make them self-explanatory (e.g. a house for housing figures or a bolt of lightning for electrical storm frequencies) and keep them simple.

3 Draw an appropriate number of symbols for the length of each bar and, if necessary, split one symbol in half but do not subdivide further.

4 Each symbol must represent, preferably, a nice easy round number like 100 or 1000, so that any half-symbols are in round numbers.

5 Keep detail to the minimum and keep the graph clear of too much information – brevity is the key!

Bear in mind that isotypes or pictographs can be time-consuming to draw. They are best used with a stencil, rub-on symbol sheet or computer, as all symbols must be identical.

Watchpoints on Charting

1 Mostly quick, visual methods to show pattern and relationships in information.

2 There are many chart and graph methods, so make sure that you are aware of the usefulness of each kind, and apply the correct one.

3 Most can be plotted as points or symbols on statistical maps and can therefore be analysed locationally as well (but the more complex can be difficult to interpret, especially as they are all over a map).

4 Use methods which may save time, rather than using unsuitable, more detailed methods, but beware because some can take time to plot.

5 Good for your final presentation report, as well as deriving your decisions.

6 Some are difficult to interpret without practice.

7 Do not be tempted to put too much in a chart – remember the need for clarity at all times, so keep it simple.

8 You sometimes see charts where the scale is

PART 2: THE SCIENCE OF GEOGRAPHICAL DECISION-MAKING

broken (with a gap), usually so that a wider range of data can be shown. This is bad practice and can lead to misinterpretation.

9 *Visual graphs and charts* are best when comparing information. *Tables* may be better when using specific or detailed figures.

10 Remember that a chart only works if it is readily understandable and the reader can follow the conventions you have used so always, on all charts, have:

- a clear title

- information on geographical coverage
- information on time period covered
- a full key to all elements used in the chart
- reference to the sources
- well labelled axes
- units of measurement shown.
- enough annotated information to help to interpret your chart.

11 A useful rule is that charts should be capable of standing on their own, without any other information, and still be comprehensible and useful.

13 *Mind Mapping*

'Mind Mapping' techniques of all kinds are much used by decision-makers to develop ideas and to stimulate decisions by focusing on the structure of the whole decision-making problem. Our minds work in complex ways to link in new ideas and spark off different avenues of enquiry, like an ever more complicated organic web rather than like a simple list or linear diagram. Mind mapping attempts to emulate this process and particularly the brain's power of complicated association of ideas. They are useful for:

- stimulating creative decision-making, even if very little comes to mind immediately

- dealing with particularly complex problems with lots of related elements

- recording all the ideas you have about a problem

- organising and grouping those ideas into a structure that is logical

- identifying the more important elements or ideas you have had on a problem

- organising your information in a way most akin to the way your mind works.

A Tree or Fishbone Chart

These simple versions of tree diagrams can be very useful in helping you to think through a problem, particularly if it is complicated. They help to clarify the major links in your information (Figure 13.1).

1 On the right hand side of your paper draw a box and write the problem to be solved inside the box.

2 Draw a horizontal line from the box to the left hand side of the paper.

3 Identify the main *factors* relevant to the problem and write each one at the end of a short line running at 45° to the original line (like the bones running along a fish backbone).

4 Identify the *secondary elements or factors* that work on each of the main factors you have identified and write these at the end of lines drawn at 45° to the factor lines.

5 Look carefully at the whole diagram and try to identify *linkages between factors* that you may not have noticed before.

Useful for:

- Trying to make sense of difficult, complex decision problems

- Focusing on the relationships of all factors and elements of the whole problem, not just its parts

- Using a familiar *linear* form of diagram to show links, easily understood

- Generating new ideas and things you had not considered.

B Mind Mapping

The method which bears this title uses a simple diagram to organize and structure ideas spontaneously, just as you think of them.

1 On a large sheet of paper, draw a circle in the centre of the page and write a short description of the problem to be solved inside the circle.

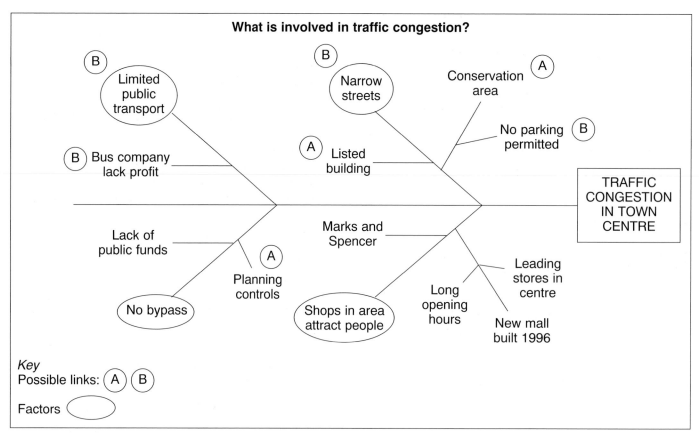

Figure 13.1 Fishbone Chart

Figure 13.2 Mind Mapping

2 As you think of related ideas or possible factors influencing the problem, draw further circles surrounding the main one and label them, linking them with a line to the central circle.

3 As you label each new circle it should act as a trigger to elements related to that particular circle and you connect further circles as you progress (Figure 13.2).

Watchpoints on Mind Mapping:

• Try to be spontaneous and creative

• Do not worry about where you should place a particular idea in the diagram, or if something that comes to mind should be included – put it all in. If you thought of it, it is probably relevant!

• Use heavier, wavey or coloured lines to indicate links you think are more important – the more you can put structure into the problem, the more it will stimulate your ideas.

• In general, the further you travel from the centre of the diagram, the more remote the relationship with the central problem.

C Strategic Choice

This method was developed during the 1960s period of growth in public participation in decision-making in planning. It is a good technique for concentrating on the relationships between sets of decisions and the uncertainties which could affect your final decision. It involves the drawing of diagrams to express the relationships involved in a decision-making problem between:

• A central problem and related decisions which might impinge on it

• The kind of uncertainties that surround these decisions

• An emphasis on the needs, preferences and ideas of people who will be affected by the decision

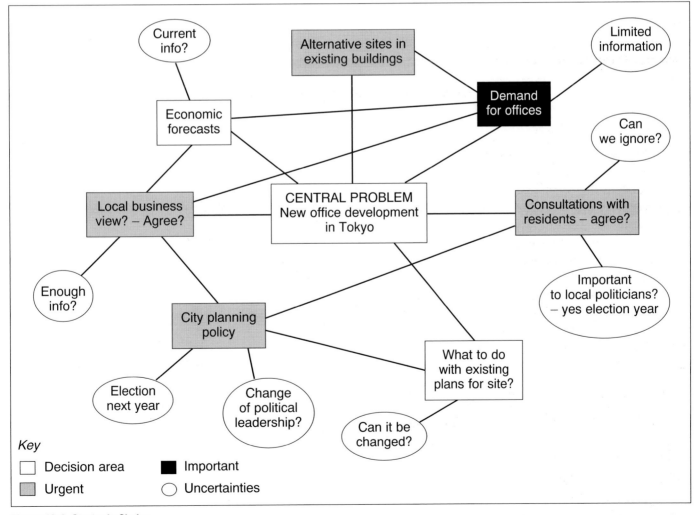

Figure 13.3 Strategic Choice

1 Draw a diagram to show all of the decision areas that you need to develop and draw each of them within a rectangle (Figure 13.3).

2 Draw lines between those decision rectangles that you think are interrelated.

3 Draw heavy lines, or shade, around those decision rectangles that you think are more urgent.

4 Draw wavey or coloured lines around, or shade, those decision rectangles that you think will, ultimately, be most important.

5 Around each rectangle, draw circles connected to the rectangle by lines, to represent the uncertainties associated with that decision.

- Uncertainties about the *Evidence* of the decision – if there are problems with, for example, the data you have to analyse for that decision, or if you will need further investigation before deciding on this element of the problem
- Uncertainties about the *Context* of the decision (e.g. political policies, rules or values held by individuals or groups that will affect the decision)

D Analysis of Interconnected Decision Areas (AIDA)

This is a useful technique for reducing complex problems to their essentials, though it is more involved than the other methods. It is a development from Strategic Choice and takes analysis one level further, by including the various options you might have within each decision area. It is most often used with problems which involve making more than one decision at the same time and problems where those individual decisions may greatly affect each other. The technique makes the overall structure of a problem clearer, identifies the relationships between the options and so focuses on the implications of each sub-decision.

1 Identify the *decision areas* (the general questions or objectives that require a decision) and draw as a diagram (Figure 13.4i). The example shows a *set of decisions* which need to be made on the location of a new factory, the date when a new school should be built, the amount of new housing required and whether this should be built by public or private agencies.

2 From this, produce a *strategy diagram* by drawing lines to link those decision areas which will affect or depend on each other to such an extent that they should really be considered together. If no link is drawn the decisions are thought to be independent of each other (Figure 13.4ii).

3 Identify the *options* possible within each decision area and draw as a diagram. It is assumed that the final answer will include one option from each decision area (Figure 13.4iii).

4 From this, produce an *options diagram* by drawing lines to link pairs of options that are incompatible, such that to choose both of them together would be unacceptable (Figure 13.4iv). It has been found to be more effective, in the options diagram, to highlight conflicts.

Figure 13.4

(i) **Analysis of Interconnected Decision Areas**

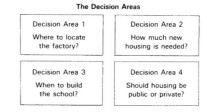

(ii) **The Strategy Diagram**

(iii) **The Options**

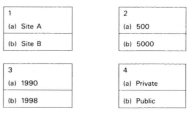

(iv) **The Options Diagram**

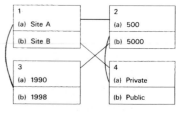

Watchpoints on Mind Mapping

1 They work like your brain – in a complex web of associations, and are therefore useful in the early stages of identifying problem and to give an overall structure to the problem scenario.

2 Good when more than one decision is to be made and especially if there are decisions of different kinds, e.g., locational, timing, quantity, urgency.

3 Very good to bring order to complex problems with many interrelated elements.

4 Focus is on relatedness of decisions and associations of ideas, so they can encourage spontaneity and unblock ideas when they are slow to come into your mind.

5 Does not evaluate options in depth and requires further methods of analysis on individual factors.

6 Use a large sheet of paper as the diagrams can look confusing if too closely drawn and use it in your final report to explain how you arrived at your decision.

7 The key to success is to be adventurous – let your mind take over, do not be restricted by the strictures of the technique, after all, they are there to help you be creative!

14 *Mapping*

Geographical problems involve information referenced to space, that is, located. The map, as a scaled-down visual representation of that geo-information, can be an extremely useful tool at most stages of the decision process. It can reduce data to meaningful quantities or categories, relate data to locations, eliminate areas from the decision process, identify important patterns, present results and even predict the consequences of decisions.

Maps can also be the canvas on which you represent the spatial distributions of data by symbols, charts or graphs derived from other decision-making methods shown in this book. They are good for:

• Providing a truly geographical representation of information

• Illustrating the spatial elements of your decision in a visually attractive illustration

• Summarising your findings

• Making clear an argument from the text

Your choice of map will depend on the measurement level of your data:

• *Nominal or ordinal data* can be shown with simple *qualitative, locational maps*. These generally employ simple shading, dot locating points or symbols or lines.

• *Interval or ratio data* will require more sophisticated *quantitative or statistical mapping*. These use more elaborate illustrative techniques.

Methods

A The Summary Map

A simple outline map onto which can be plotted different data sets or information derived from other maps and decision-making methods in order to identify or illustrate spatial patterns and relationships. A well annotated summary map should always be part of a decision report on a geographical problem. It can be either qualitative or quantitative in style, depending on the data to be shown.

QUALITATIVE MAPS

Qualitative maps simply locate information, though they can become quite complex and detailed. They show the:

• nature or kind of data

• location of the data and, generally, use:

• categorical data.

They can be modified by introducing a simple scale of symbol, shading or line, but do not generally work well if you wish to show detailed quantities of data located on your map (for that you need *quantitative maps*).

B The Dot Map

These deceptively simple maps show information as constant sized dots, each dot representing one occurrence of a feature. They can be useful to show spatial distributions and to identify locational clusters of data from the map.

1 Choose a suitable scale for the dots. Ensure that they will all fit on the map. Choose how many units of your data each dot will represent (for example, 10 people or 1000 people.)

2 Try out the lowest and highest densities of dots on your map to ensure that they are not either 'lost' or over-congested.

3 Calculate the number of dots per area on the map.

4 Draw them evenly spaced (do not put in linear fashion), or try to adopt a suitable, natural distribution over the areas involved (for example, there may be an obvious urban magnetism to the pattern of horticultural production in a basically rural area).

Possible problems with dot maps:

1 Placing of dots can be misleading – are you sure that the distribution is even over the administrative area? Should you place them evenly, or use your good sense to place them more naturally?

2 Too small a dot value, or too large a size of dot can give a poor visual impression by crowding parts of the map.

3 Can be modified by including different coloured dots to give more refinement.

The Choropleth Map

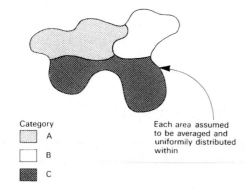

Category
A
B
C

Each area assumed to be averaged and uniformily distributed within

Figure 14.1

C The Symbol Map

These are a variation on the simple dot map, where information is shown with suitable symbols to replace the dots. For example, sheep for sheep production figures, houses for built-up areas. Use the same method as for dot maps, but:

• Make sure that your symbol is instantly recognizable as representing your data, otherwise why bother?

• Keep them of a suitable size, otherwise they can really spoil the effect by becoming too obtrusive.

• Make sure that you use a computer symbol set or dry-transfer sheets, or even stencils, as all symbols MUST be identical.

D The Line Map

Line maps may show simple linear features such as roads, railways or routes as discrete features without scale variation.

• They can, however, be modified to show the relative size or scale of the lines by varying the width or colour of the lines.

• Useful to show *flows* along lines, *size of flow* by width of line and *direction of flow* by arrows along the lines.

E The Choropleth Map

A map using shading to identify areas with similar characteristics.

• Easy to construct and visually attractive, but assumes data is averaged and uniform within each area shaded.

• Quantity is usually expressed as *density per unit area*, or some measure that is independent of area, like *percentages or ratios*.

• Categories can be defined by evenly spaced limits, quartiles, nominal or ordinal scaling or other classification methods (see *Classification*).

• If data is continuous (e.g., population density) shading should follow meaningful density scales; if data is discrete (e.g., party voting) shading should show clear distinction as in Figure 14.1.

• Data must be grouped into classes with known intervals that are clearly shown in the key.

1 Calculate the range of your data.

2 Decide on the number of classes you will need to show.

3 Choose appropriate interval ranges for each class.

4 Select appropriate shading for each class.

5 Shade each area completely with its shading symbol.

Be careful with choropleth maps:

1 Best for data that can be averaged over areas, with limited detail.

2 Very dependent for success on choice of categories, i.e. *classification*.

3 Assumes whole area is identical in each shaded portion and presumes a uniform distribution within each area.

4 Shading must follow a logical sequence, so that the sequence of the data is mirrored – for example, high values represented by heavy shading which scales down to light shading for low values.

F The Sieve Map

Sometimes called a *filter map,* it works just as a set of sieves works: each sieve removes a different size of particle, each stage of the sieve map eliminates another section of the area from the decision process (Figure 14.2). An overlay of each feature that makes an area unsuitable for the development proposed is laid over the map in turn and the area covered is shaded. The area left unshaded must therefore be available for the proposal. Areas shaded more than once would show more sensitive areas needing more protection.

Sieve mapping is a widely-used and useful hand-method closely akin to the computerised *Geographical Information System* (Section 21) and to *Probability Maps* (Section 14 .I) and *Route-Finding CPA* (Section 16).

Watch out with sieve maps:

1 Always begin with elimination criteria which cover the largest part of the map, so identifying and eliminating large areas first.

2 Simple, quick and effective for locational problems.

The Sieve Map

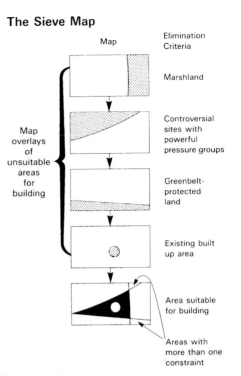

Figure 14.2

3 Best where objectives, and therefore elimination criteria, are clear.

4 Problems where much of the information is in map form are most amenable to sieve mapping.

5 A coarse method, not for use with detailed variables or non-locatable information.

6 Assumes that all elimination criteria are of equal importance – this can be overcome by weighting the criteria on a scale of 1 to 5, adding up numbers where criteria overlap and, if say, you are finding a road route, avoiding those areas with the highest numbers.

7 Assumes that all elimination criteria are homogeneous (that is, they are equally important over their whole area) – this can be overcome by using the weighting method in 6 above, but ranking each square of a suitably sized grid of squares inside each criterion area (as in the section on Probability Mapping).

QUANTITATIVE MAPS

Quantitative or statistical mapping takes longer to calculate and draw, but can show the:

• nature of the data

• location of the data

- quantity of the data and can use:
- continuous data

G *Proportional Symbol Maps*

When using data located at a number of points, symbols of varying size, or proportion, can be used to add *quantity* to your map. Different values can be shown by different sized symbols and/or different shading, and virtually all of the charts and graphs shown elsewhere in this book can be transformed into symbols for locating on maps (though many, if you think about it, would be too complex to be useful – remember that it is simplicity that gives impact to a map).

Pros:

- Useful to show quite complex information
- Useful to show a wide range of data values
- Can be visually impressive

Cons:

- Sometimes time-consuming to produce
- Sometimes too complex
- Need very careful placing of the symbols
- Do not normally overlap symbols – all should be clear

If possible, put some scale line, gradient line or other key to the range of symbol sizes you are using – otherwise they are notoriously difficult to compare with each other and to identify the exact size of each symbol. Equally, it can help to annotate each symbol with its actual value.

Proportional Bars

- Use the method for *Bar Graphs* and locate each on the map
- Scale of bars is a problem – remember they all have to fit on the map
- Wide range in data can be difficult to show adequately
- Draw bars vertically on a map – horizontal bars are difficult to interpret if on a map background

Proportional Circles

- Here the *area of the circle* represents the value of the data

- The square roots of the values is used to derive the circle size, it can therefore show a wider range of data as the area measurement compresses ranges visually
- The radius of each circle is the square root of each value, after dividing it by 3.142:

$$\sqrt{\frac{Value}{3.142}}$$

- Carefully consider the size of circles that can be shown on your map
- They can be more difficult to interpret as small variations in size, on different areas of a map, can be hard to distinguish

Proportional Squares

- As above, for circles, but here the size is calculated as the *area of the square*
- The length of each side equals the square root of the value:

$$\sqrt{Value}$$

Proportional Triangles

- Equilateral triangles can show different sized values as the *area of the triangles*
- Here the length of the side is the square root of the value, after multiplying it by 2.309:

$$\sqrt{Value \times 2.309}$$

Proportional Pie Graphs

- As in the *Pie Graph* section, located on the map
- The overall size of each pie can also be varied as in *Proportional Circles* above
- But, the more complex, the less effective!

Proportional Spheres

Because these are solid objects, it is their *volume* that gives the value to each symbol, therefore:

- They can cope with a much larger range of values, but:
- They are more difficult to draw
- They are even more difficult to interpret, as volume is not easily appreciated when comparing objects visually
- Use the formula:

$$\sqrt[3]{\frac{value \times 3}{12.56}}$$

- Multiply the value by 3, divide by 12.56 and find the cube root of the result. The final result is the radius of the Proportional Sphere.

Proportional Cubes

These are also solid objects, so it is their *volume* that gives the value to each symbol, therefore:

- They can cope with a much larger range of values, but:

- They are more difficult to draw

- They are even more difficult to interpret as volume is not easy to compare between objects

- Use the formula:

$$\sqrt[3]{value}$$

- The cubed root of the value gives the length of each side of the Proportional Cube.

H The Isopleth Map

The Isopleth Map

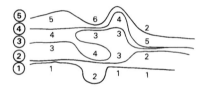

Figure 14.3

The Isopleth or *Isoline map* is used where detailed point data is provided and it joins places of equal value on whichever scale is used (Figure 14.3). The word isoline means 'lines of equal value' and these maps are used with *continuous data*, that is, data like temperatures, heights or population densities, which can all be seen as occurring all over the map, even if only measured at a few points (imagine the data as representing columns of different heights, holding up a canvas over the whole area, so that you get an impression of relative heights over the whole map – if that appears logical to you, for your data, then use an isopleth map).

1 Plot the values at each point on the map and annotate or use symbols to show the varying values.

2 Choose intervals for the isolines suitable for your data and map area.

3 Draw lines to join places of equal value. You will rarely find that you have enough of each value so you will need to interpolate:

- Assume that the gradient between points of which you know the value is constant
- Carefully place each line at the appropriate distance from each point
- Never split isolines
- Never omit isolines, even where very congested
- Annotate appropriately, but not every line

Be careful with isopleth maps:

1 Can be used with detailed point data.

2 Best with data which is continuous (e.g., height, temperature, land costs). More discrete or fluctuating data can be confusing or misleading.

3 Like contours, can show patterns of distribution and rates of change of values over space.

I The Probability Map

Also known as the *Monte Carlo technique*, since it incorporates a chance element (Figure 14.4) as in gambling. An excellent method to allow the decision-maker to *simulate the possible results of decisions*. The example shows proximity to built-up area as a positive criterion for a new housing estate, and nearness to marshland as a negative one – where might it be located?

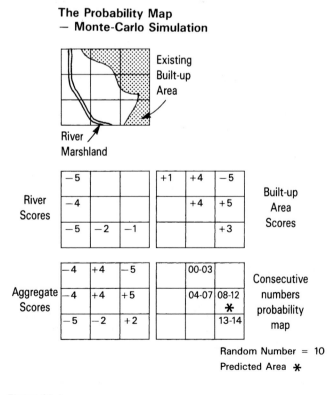

Figure 14.4

1 List criteria, positive and negative and map these.

2 Divide the map up into grid squares of suitable size.

3 Score each grid square on each criterion, ranging from −5 for very negative, to +5 for very positive factors.

4 Add up these scores, eliminate any square at or below 0.

5 Express the scores as consecutive numbers so that any individual number only appears once on the map.

6 Use random number tables to choose the number for the housing. As random numbers are used any square may be chosen but the map is weighted by the criteria, so the probability is highest that the square with 08–12 would be chosen.

Things to watch with probability maps:

1 Simple way to try out the effects of your decisions, since the simulation could be rerun with different criteria or options.

2 Retains an element of chance, bringing it *closer to reality.*

3 Adds *simulation* to the decision-maker's armoury.

J The Topological Map

A *topographical map* of London would show streets, railway stations and places in their true relative positions. The familiar London underground map is a *topological map*, transforming space to make the network clearer and simpler to use. The topographical example (Figure 14.5) is transformed to simply show which places have direct routes between them. This isolates the essence of the routeways and shows clearly that A has the most connections. Similar transformations can give different perspectives:

- rail routes measured as time taken, or cost of journey, rather than physical distance

- countries of the world drawn scaled on size of GNP or population rather than physical area.

Points to watch with topological maps:

1 Can be time consuming to construct.

2 Best in the presentation of decisions.

3 Requires some lateral thinking and individuals vary in their ability to work this way.

4 A creative technique which demands that the decision-maker free him or herself from the 'normal' mapping by linear distance. As such it can be fascinating, but be sure that it is relevant to the problem in hand.

Watchpoints on Mapping

1 All maps should be clear, precise and efficient and should have:

- A clear title
- Scale information (in words, scale line or representative fraction)
- Orientation – usually by compass direction
- A key of symbols/shading
- Identified source of information
- Appropriate annotation

2 Maps should:

- show your information without distortion
- be visually attractive
- focus the reader directly onto the substance of your argument
- make complex information understandable
- be closely integrated with the written parts of your report

The Topological Map

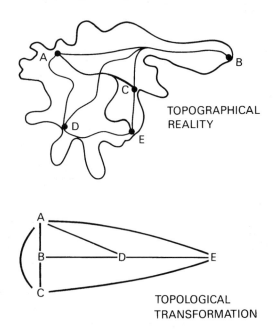

TOPOGRAPHICAL REALITY

TOPOLOGICAL TRANSFORMATION

Figure 14.5

So do use maps to:

- consolidate and simplify large data sets when location is important
- summarize, yet show some detail also from the data sets
- identify 'outliers' – those areas or features that are anomolous or different, which might not be easy to spot in a table or chart
- make an impact

But do not use maps:

- with small data sets – the result is probably already very obvious so why waste time?
- when location is not important or is irrelevant to a problem
- simply to make an impact
- just 'because its geography'!

15 Decision Tree

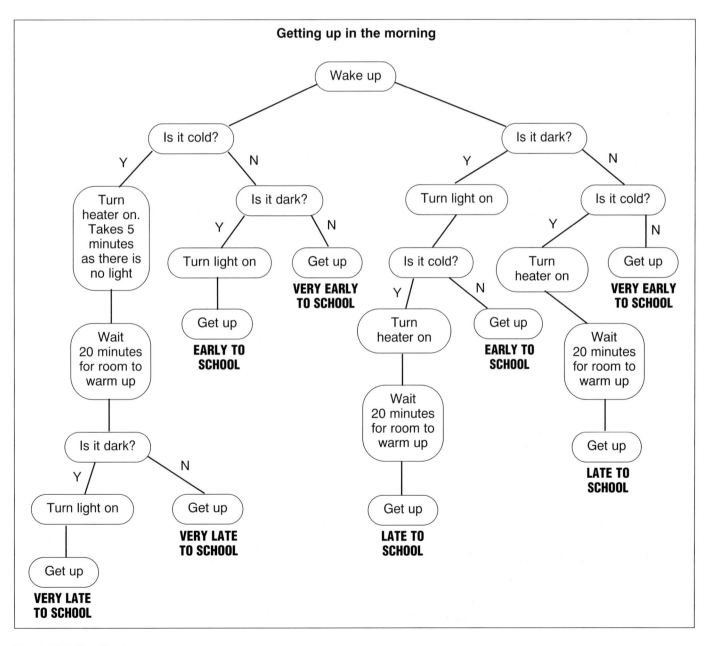

Figure 15.1 Flow Chart

Techniques used to chart a sequence of decisions occurring in time, they concentrate on the consequences of each decision and incorporate uncertain external events which might affect outcomes. These diagrammatic methods break down decision problems and, by calculating outcomes at each decision point, can help to isolate the best option in a structured, controlled way.

A Flow Charts

Simple trees which show the sequence of operations or factors in order to highlight the points at which decisions will be required in the process. They can be useful to identify all the possible results from a set of conditions and the subsequent decisions necessary, and they ensure that no decision in a set is omitted in the flow of activities. They are sometimes called *chain diagrams*, since they show logical stages in the process of decision-making and simple consequences of that chain of events and decisions.

Though they can use probability scaling on branches of the tree, they are, generally, more limited since they concentrate on flow in a linear form and sequence, and simple outcomes that are reasonably predictable, rather than on the interaction between events and decisions, which is often, in Geography, more complex and distinctly non-linear.

The example flow chart here (Figure 15.1), of how one gets out of bed in the morning, has simple 'yes/no' possibility decisions based on the light and temperature (chance) conditions possible early in the morning, the resultant decisions and the end product.

Things to be aware of with flow charts:

1 Much depends on your first choice – do you check the darkness or the coldness first?

2 The most influential chance condition occurs when it is both cold and dark, so to remedy these we need to put the light and heating on, and then wait while the room warms up, making us late in rising.

3 This is made worse if we try to solve the lack of warmth problem before the lack of light problem, as we have difficulty turning the heating on in the dark!

4 This is a very simple example, but it shows that some of the flows may be more crucial than others – these are the *critical path* elements of the flow chart and will be discussed in detail in Section 16.

B Decision Trees

These are more complex and more useful, as they quantify the outcomes of each decision and allow identification of the critical paths. They thus show better the two-way interaction between your decision choices and the chance events. Figure 15.2 shows a simple tree for deciding whether to stay in bed or go for a walk, under different chance weather conditions.

A Decision Tree

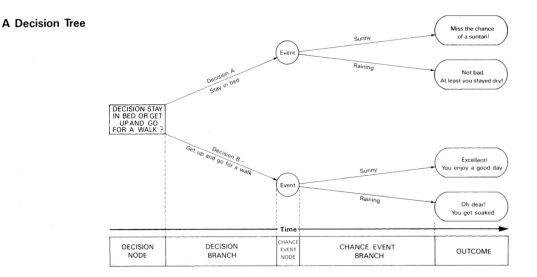

Figure 15.2

Method

1 Make a list of the *decisions* to be made and the possible external *chance events* which might occur. Place them in approximate chronological (time) order.

2 Construct the decision tree, starting at the left of the diagram and using *nodes* and *branches*.

- Nodes where you have to make a *decision* are drawn in *boxes or diamonds*.
- Nodes for *chance events*, over which you have no control, are usually drawn inside *circles*.
- Terminal nodes of the final result or outcome are usually drawn in horizontal *ellipses*.

3 From each decision box draw lines to represent the alternative choices – these are your *action branches*, dependent on your choices.

4 From each event-circle draw lines to represent each possible chance outcome, these are your *outcome branches*, dependent on chance occurences.

5 Scale each branch either on a *desirability/utility* or, more usually, *probability* basis. Figure 15.3 extends the problem to include two more uncertain events: your friends mentioned they might call on you and your Dad might give you some money to go out with. It was sunny yesterday, so it might be today, your friends might be influenced by the weather and your Dad might be influenced by whether you appear lazy or if your friends turn up. What would you do?

6 Analyse the tree. Remember that the probability of a number of uncertain events all occurring together is the *product* of their individual probabilities so, the value of a particular decision node is equal to the *product of all the following nodes.*

7 So the most probable outcome is a sunny day, your friends visit and you get your funds from Dad – that is, if you choose to get up! Then p = 0.6 × 0.8 × 0.9 = 0.432, quite a high score and the highest pay-off of all. If you choose to stay in bed, then your best pay-off, even with most events favourable, is only p = 0.288 (0.6 × 0.8 × 0.6 = 0.288). So you know what to do!

8 A decision tree can include more than one decision node.

9 The number of ultimate outcomes in every case is two (for example 0.144 and 0.096 on the line at the base of the diagram) and therefore, your final decision will depend on whether you are a *maximax* or *maximin* decision-maker – do you want the highest return or do you want a lesser return with more stability?

10 Notice that both of the worst outcomes (p = 0.024) occur if you stay in bed. If you had decided to wear a raincoat, it would affect the chance that you would get wet, but would have no effect on the chance of it raining (this would need another set of decision nodes and branches).

Probabilities on a Decision Tree

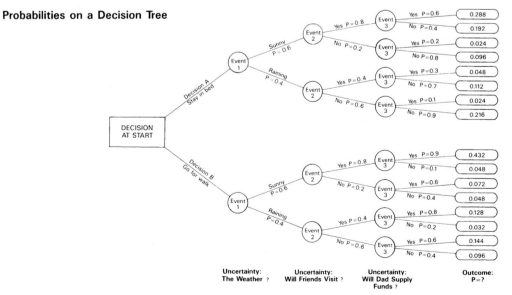

Figure 15.3

Watchpoints on Decision Trees

1 Label and annotate your diagram clearly, to ensure that you can see all the implications of each stage in the decision-making process.

2 Check that at each stage the total probabilities add up to 1. Remember that a decimal probability is like a percentage with a decimal point in front of it, so a 75% chance that a sea wall will be breached at high tide is a .75 probability, a 4% chance is a .04 probability and a 90.5% chance is a .905 probability.

3 Good technique for looking at, for example, the complex consequences of decisions in environmental uncertainties over time, as it can throw up new ideas from the discipline of formal analysing of alternatives.

4 Time flows from left to right so by 'rolling back' (following the paths right–left) it is possible to identify key events, decisions or paths in the whole process.

5 The tree is not an answer-machine, but an aid to comparing the consequences of paths of decision in time.

6 The optimum decision that a decision tree identifies may still not be the most appropriate in a complex problem.

7 Can be informative, particularly where decisions are independent of one another, and where some measure of the risks and returns at each decision stage are important.

8 Focus is on how each decision affects what comes next, and reducing uncertainty to a minimum.

9 Note that each decision or event node may have more than two outcome branches.

10 Use a large sheet of paper; even simple trees can rapidly expand!

11 If time is limited, the tree, or even a simple flowchart, can be useful, even without probability calculations, as they make you identify options, decisions and influential factors or events in a clear and logical manner.

12 It is also possible to incorporate scoring systems based both upon the probability of chance events and the desirability of the consequences of individual decisions. To evaluate outcomes, multiply the desirability score by the probability score on each decision branch and choose that with the highest score.

16 Critical Path Analysis (CPA)

The techniques in this section can help to plan and manage a project or decide on a problem, particularly when time and cost are important and when you have to look at the sequencing of activities in managing your project. This can be simple, like making yourself a cup of tea while you ponder your decision, or extremely complex, like building a new town or stabilizing a hillside prone to slipping. They can help to answer questions like, how long will it take? If one activity is delayed will the project succeed? Which are the most essential tasks?

A Critical Path Analysis (CPA)

Like the decision tree, CPA concentrates on problems involving sequential decisions but also attempts to identify the chain of decisions and events that is most critical to the solution of the complete network of decisions and events, and the minimum time needed to complete it.

CPA identifies the sequences of actions that follow one another (for example, you cannot boil a kettle without first filling it) and finds the path that is the most essential to the project staying on schedule. It is thus of great use in managing the implementation of large projects and in evaluating the feasibility of implementing, say, a motorway scheme, within a specified time scale.

Critical Path Analysis for Making a Cup of Tea

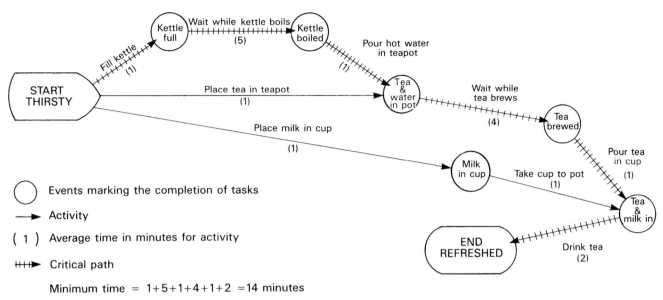

Events marking the completion of tasks

→ Activity

(1) Average time in minutes for activity

╫╫▶ Critical path

Minimum time = 1+5+1+4+1+2 =14 minutes

Figure 16.1

Programme Evaluation and Review Technique (PERT)

This is a variant of the normal CPA and goes further to use probability (by defining the optimistic and pessimistic range within which we expect to accomplish a task) and costings for each stage. It can analyse slack times in the network, during which other activities could occur and show overlaps in time to give some flexibility to solving the problem. However, in both CPA and PERT, the critical path is still the essential and shortest route possible to complete the project, which must be completed on time for the project as a whole to be completed on time.

Method

1 Identify each decision or action that is required.

2 Identify the events that mark the completion of each stage of activity.

3 Establish which activity *must* precede which other activities.

4 Establish the time needed for each activity, or, if it is important, the resources needed for each activity, or its financial cost.

5 Draw as a diagram.

6 Identify the *critical path,* that is often the path that involves most activities or includes the basic, essential activities necessary to the whole project or the activities which collectively must precede the rest.

7 Decide on project schedule.

For example: How would you make a cup of tea? What would you do first? Boil the water? find the cups? Most of us would say 'Fill the kettle'. Why? Figure 16.1 follows this simple decision-making problem and shows how that action is the start of the 'critical path'. If you do not do that first and ensure that you complete that particular path, then the whole project will take much longer!

The kettle critical path involves most time in its sequence and includes periods of waiting (when other tasks can be accomplished) and most other activities need only be completed some time before the kettle finally boils. 'Milk in cup' and 'take cup to pot' take only one minute each and could be done any time during the 'kettle boils' or 'tea brews' phases, while 'tea in pot' can occur any time during the five-minute 'kettle boils' phase.

Gannt Chart
Building a Sports Hall

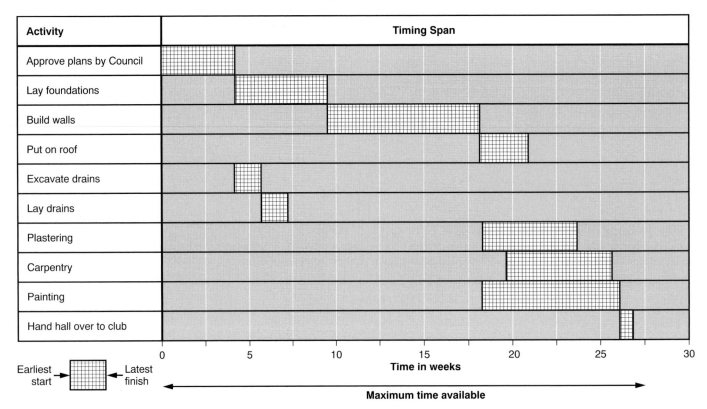

Figure 16.2

B Gannt Charts

These specialised charts are used with both CPA and PERT to display the timetable graphically so that we can compare different elements of a project and find overlaps and slack periods. Developed by Henry Gantt, they are sometimes, improperly, called *bar charts*, as they show activities on a timescale by using bars to showing possible start and end times.

1 Construct a grid with two axes. Figure 16.2 shows the activities required in the building of a new sports hall in a village:

- the horizontal axis is always time periods
- the vertical axis should list the activities necessary for the project

2 Start the list of activities with those you think should begin first at the top, the later activities below, separating those that clearly must be finished before others can begin (in our example, the Council must approve the plans before we start any work on site, and we cannot bring in bricklayers for the walls until the foundations are

in, and, until the walls are up, we cannot put on the roof, but the plastering, carpentry and painting can overlap).

3 Draw bars to represent the start and end times for each project activity.

4 Look at each activity in turn and decide which, perhaps because they use the same people or machines in our example, could not be carried out concurrently.

5 Separate these on the timeline.

6 Use the chart to identify where you might make different decisions, start or end times, or both.

C Route Finding CPA

As critical path analysis is, essentially, a method for finding the optimum path through a complex network of decisions, it can work equally well, with some modification, with spatial problems and the identification of best routes through a transport network between nodes. A variety of these route-finding CPA methods is illustrated overleaf.

These variations of critical path analysis focus on finding the best routes between nodes in a locational network context, and are therefore useful in many geographical problems. The problem might be to find the shortest, the cheapest or the fastest route from one town to another, or to find a holiday route for tourists or to identify the best way to link all places in an area with a new oil pipeline.

Computer programs like *Autoroute* (Nextbase Limited) employ many more sophisticated versions of these methods to find routes, and employ detailed databases. The methods below are intended for simple analyses that can be undertaken by hand in a short time period.

C1 The Minimal Connecting CPA In Figure 16.3, we have a simple set of places marked A to E. The problem facing the oil company is how to connect all the places by pipeline, using the minimum of pipe.

1 Go to any place, let us choose A, and connect it to its nearest place, which here is E.

2 Find the place which is closest to the last place you connected (E), which is B, and connect that.

3 Continue step 2 until there are no unconnected places left.

4 If there are unconnected places closer to connected places other than the last one you connected, then link that new place to its closest place (in the example, we connect A to E to B to C, but find that C is now, at best, 150 miles from its nearest neighbour, so we look to D to see that a link to E is closer than 150 miles).

5 You can verify your result by starting at any place – you will always find this the shortest connecting network and the critical path for the pipeline.

C2 The Travelling Salesman CPA Minimal Connecting Paths have a single objective – minimizing the total length of connections, irrespective of whether places are visited twice in following the route. The famous *travelling salesman* problem is different: the salesman wants to spend the minimum time travelling (so wants the smallest total travel route) and wants to visit all places, but only once, and to find the best order in which to visit the places. How do we find the best route now?

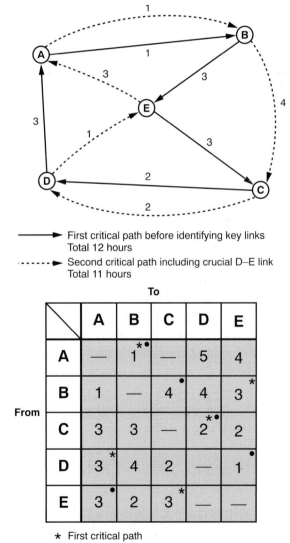

First critical path before identifying key links
Total 12 hours

Second critical path including crucial D–E link
Total 11 hours

To

From		A	B	C	D	E
	A	—	1 *•	—	5	4
	B	1	—	4 •	4	3 *
	C	3	3	—	2 *•	2
	D	3 *	4	2	—	1 •
	E	3 •	2	3 *	—	—

★ First critical path
• Second critical path including crucial D–E link (shortest links: A to B, D to E)
— No flight in that direction
Note: flight times between some places vary

Figure 16.4

Minimal Connecting CPA

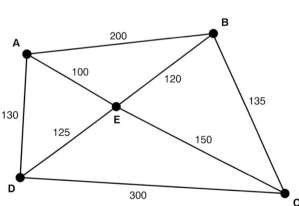

Total route: 480 miles (A–E–B–C + D–E)

Figure 16.3

Figure 16.4 shows a similar problem: a tourist wants to visit all of the towns in the region, starting and ending at A, wants as little time travelling as possible and does not want to go to any single place more than once. What route should they take?

1 As time is important to the tourist, measure distances by time and insert in a cross-tabulation. Note that you are inserting times from every place to every other place and so journeys in reverse directions between two places may differ (e.g., flights may vary in directness of route or be dependant on the direction of the prevailing winds).

2 Start at A, in the left hand column, and identify the shortest time route to another place (here B).

3 From B, again in the right hand column, identify the shortest time to another place so far unvisited, here E.

4 Continue until all places are visited.

5 Note that this gives a tourist route of A to B to E to C to D to A and a total travel time of 12 hours.

6 However, this assumes a simple closest place each time in sequence, starting with A, and it may be that we have to employ other means to get an even shorter route:

1 Check the table for all critical path links – minimum time links. Here we have the link A to B as 1 hour, but we also have link D to E which has only 1 hour – this is also a critical path link and so *must* be included in our path.

2 Recalculate from stage 2, starting at A, but ensuring that D to E is one of the links (note it is not E to D, which is a longer journey!). There are two choices:

   • A to B to D to E to C to D to A (there is no direct link A to C) with a total travel time of 14 hours – clearly a worse route
   • A to B to C to D to E to A with a total travel time of 11 hours – our obvious choice and better than our first attempt!

C3 Shortest Route CPA Finding a shortest route path is a common problem – how do we travel from one place (A) to another place (B) by the shortest, or cheapest or fastest route? There are two simple methods:

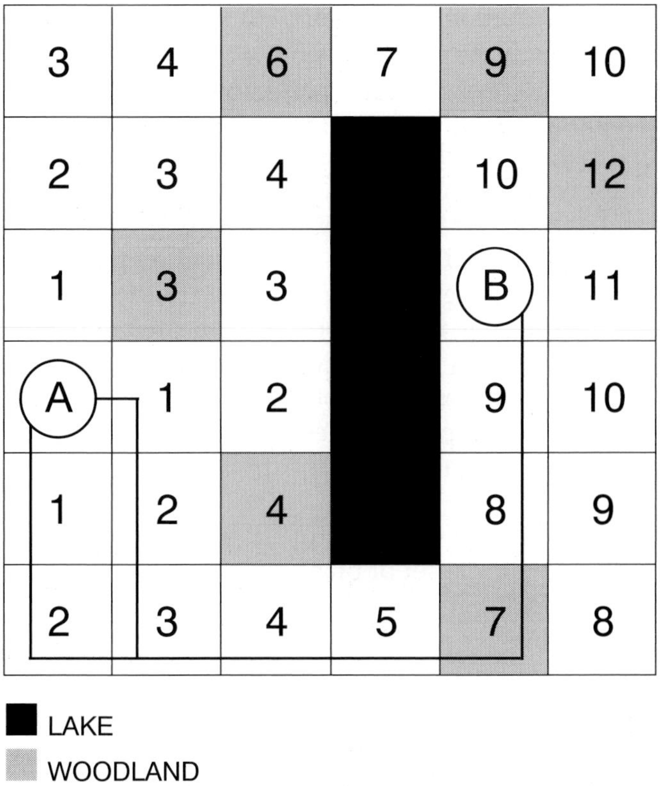

■ LAKE

▨ WOODLAND

Figure 16.5 Shortest Route CPA Grid-Map Method

The Grid-Map Method (Figure 16.5) can be used when linear distance is important and we have a map of the area.

1 Draw a grid of squares over the map and mark the positions of A and B.

2 Shade squares that are *impossible to travel over*. In our example, the squares with a lake. Ignore these squares from now on.

3 Shade, in a different pattern, squares which are *difficult, but not impossible, to traverse*, here the squares with woodland.

4 Starting at A, put a figure '1' in each square that is one step from A (i.e. those adjacent horizontally or vertically – ignore the diagonal as those squares are further away).

5 Put a '2' in all squares adjacent to those with a '1' and, so far, without a number in them.

6 Put '3's in the next set of squares and continue until the map is complete.

7 Squares that are difficult to cross (our woodland) should have an extra '1' added to their score.

8 You now have a *probability map* of travel in the area, with all possible routes costed in units of distance, the difficult ones costed higher and the impossible ones out of the picture.

9 Now work backwards from B, marking your route along the path of squares which each have a value lower than the one you are currently within.

10 In our example, there are two possible ends to our journey after the square with a '3', so both are marked – both routes have a length or cost of 39 and both are valid answers.

The Network Method (Figure 16.6) is used when distances are measured in time or cost units, where simple linear distance is not a useful measure of links, or when a map is not available. The example is an area of highland, bog and estuary, and we need to travel by the quickest route from A to B.

1 Draw a network of the links, with the travel time between nodes that are connected by land or water directly (note water travel takes longer).

2 Draw a table of the shortest distances to all nodes in one, two and three steps from the starting point, A.

3 Continue adding more steps to the table until the last column is an exact replica of the one before it. This is then used to work out the critical path (in our example, the 3 and 4 step columns are identical).

4 Looking at the network and times, the shortest time to arrive at B from A is 230 minutes (3 steps). Working back, we could get there via F, C or E, but do they all give us enough time?:

• we would have to arrive at F by 230 − 90 = 140 minutes
• at C by 230 − 180 = 50 minutes (clearly, the route via C is impossible since it takes 100 minutes to travel from A to C)
• at E by 230 − 100 = 130 minutes so that we would be on time (but, similarly, the route via E is not workable as we need 225 minutes to get to E from A)

5 The route is therefore A to C to F to B, taking 230 minutes

Topographical Map
Shortest Route CPA Network Method

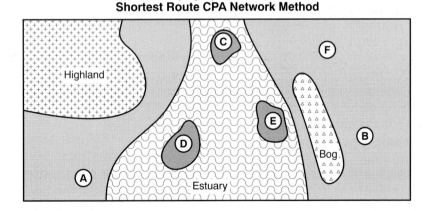

Shortest Path Times to Nodes
From A in 1 to 4 Steps

Place	Steps 1	2	3	4
A	0	0	0	∞
B	∞	280	230	230
C	100	100	100	100
D	75	75	75	75
E	∞	150	150	150
F	∞	140	140	140

∞ = infinity (no one or two step links)

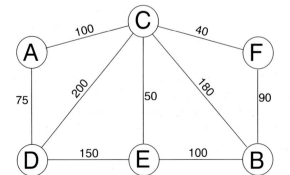

Figure 16.6

Watchpoints on CPA

1 Scheduling expensive projects involves a sequence of decisions and decisions on the timing of actions; traditional CPA is therefore of most use in assessing ways to implement proposals.

2 CPA concentrates on sequence and timing, while the *decision tree* focuses on sequence and consequence.

3 Route-finding CPA can be done in a variety of ways – choose the method which can be done in the time available and which is best for the specific information you are given.

4 Beyond simple schemes, CPA of any kind may require a computer to analyse the data adequately. The Microsoft program *Microsoft Project* incorporates CPA, PERT and Gannt Charts methods.

5 Good for:

- isolating the key sequence of decisions from the lesser decisions in a problem
- deciding the order in which elements of a problem must be tackled
- showing the fastest route to a solution or a location
- identifying which activities can be undertaken in parallel
- showing you how you might respond if a particular activity is behind schedule or more difficult than you imagined.
- map-based analysis of routes and links between places.

17 *Cost-Benefit Analysis (CBA)*

This is a technique to use to assess the desirability of a project by examining the overall social/ economic costs to the community and the social/ economic benefits that might be made. It concentrates on measuring or quantifying *externalities*, that is, the good and bad effects on the community as a whole. It is essentially about the economic optimising of resources (as a result, it is sometimes called *social cost-benefit analysis*). It therefore strives to put a monetary value on factors and is often used as part of an EIA.

It owes much to economists and particularly to Vifredo Pareto, from whose name comes the term Pareto Optimality, which is the idea that it is impossible to make one person or group in society better off without making some other person or group worse off. This does not mean that we can necessarily achieve a best distribution, but that we can at least try to achieve the balance that would be acceptable.

The biggest problem is finding kinds of objective and subjective measures of factors when purely financial or other market measures are not available. Costs and benefits which cannot be measured, priced or valued are termed *intangibles*, and a number of methods can be used to put a value on such factors:

- *opportunity cost* (valuing a proposal by estimating the lost benefits of not using alternative proposals)

- *contingent valuation* (questioning people on what they would be prepared to pay for something)

- *multipliers* (e.g. additional profits to, say, a shop, from increasing employment in an industry)

Method

1 Define the scope and objectives of the proposals

2 Draw up a matrix with three columns:

- Column one is a simple list of all the relevant *elements* that might be changed, or *individuals or groups* that will be affected
- Column two identifies the expected *benefits* (positive or good changes) that will come with each element if the project proceeds
- Column three identifies the *costs* (negative or bad changes) that will come with each element if the project proceeds.

3 In Columns two and three place a value on each cost and benefit. Value is usually measured in money terms, but simple ranking and/or rating that you devise can give good results.

4 Calculate the Total Benefits and the Total Costs as an approximate measure to help you decide and then calculate two special measures:

- *Utility*, which is the total benefits minus the total costs (a positive result shows greater benefits than costs)
- The *cost-benefit ratio*,which is the total benefits divided by the total costs.

5 Use as an aid to deciding.

6 There are two different styles of CBA that you can use:

- The *Pareto Balance Sheet* which compares profit and loss for individual interested parties who will be affected (Figure 17.1) and whose profits/losses you will need to balance with the good of the whole community. This uses the individuals or groups in Column 1.
- The *Social Cost-Benefit Matrix* which balances the profits and losses to the community as a whole (Figure 17.2). This uses the different elements of the proposal in Column 1.

Watchpoints on CBA

1 In a full CBA, values would need to be 'discounted' to a common date, because some costs and benefits may only materialize many years later, but ignore this in simple problems.

2 What is a beneficial decision? Is it good if someone gains and nobody loses? If somebody loses, is it still good if the gainers compensate the losers? Or do we simply ensure that, on balance, the community as a whole gains rather than loses (even though some may simply lose)? There can be difficult ethical and social decisions to be made!

Pareto Balance Sheet

Interested Party	Benefits (Gains in £)		Costs (Losses in £)	
LORD CRENSHAM, Landowner	Land Sale	£	Agricultural Production	£
	House Value Increase	£		
	TOTAL BENEFITS	£	TOTAL COSTS	£
UTILITY (BENEFITS – COSTS) :				
C/B RATIO (BENEFITS ÷ COSTS) :				

Focus on **individual** costs and benefits

Figure 17.1

Social Cost Benefit Analysis

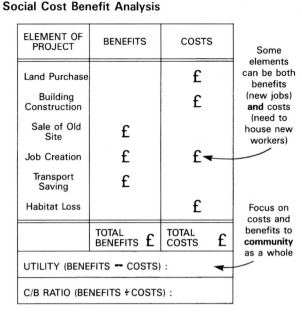

ELEMENT OF PROJECT	BENEFITS	COSTS
Land Purchase		£
Building Construction		£
Sale of Old Site	£	
Job Creation	£	£
Transport Saving	£	
Habitat Loss		£
TOTAL BENEFITS £		TOTAL COSTS £
UTILITY (BENEFITS – COSTS) :		
C/B RATIO (BENEFITS ÷ COSTS) :		

Some elements can be both benefits (new jobs) **and** costs (need to house new workers)

Focus on costs and benefits to **community** as a whole

MONETARY VALUE (£) MAY BE REPLACED BY SIMPLE ORDINAL (RANK) SCALING

Figure 17.2

3 Do not give undue weight to elements simply because they are easier to value.

4 There is a tendency to undervalue benefits and exaggerate costs in CBA, as costs are often easier to quantify.

5 A good comprehensive technique which tries to focus on the ultimate benefit to the community and on overall welfare.

6 A deceptively simple technique to grasp, but requires close attention to scaling and valuation.

7 Inputs can be difficult to value – what costs/benefits are relevant? How do you value intangibles like the beauty of the countryside, noise, loss of amenity, psychological worry, a church or a quiet night's sleep near an airport?

8 You may need to distinguish:

- *tangible* (e.g., electricity produced by a new power station) and *intangible* (e.g., power station pollution) values

- *direct* (e.g., jobs in the power station) and *indirect* (e.g., jobs in local shops as a result of power workers spending money) values

9 Much depends on the scenario of the decision-making problem. You will frequently have to decide which is more important – one person's or group's benefits or another's costs? Are

political factors, or environmental, or commercial more important than the others?

10 Much also rests on your own views of social justice – exactly what *is* best for society?

Figure 17.3 shows an early example of CBA in action – the analysis done for the Roskill Commission which had to decide on which of the four alternative sites should be chosen for the Third London Airport in 1970.

Using CBA and other methods, the Commission recommended Cublington (you can see that it comes out of the CBA as the most economically cost-effective). However, as often happens, political rather than economic factors weighed heavier with the government and they rejected the recommendations in favour of the coastal Foulness site (which was, in CBA terms, the most costly). In the event, there was a general economic downturn and the Third London Airport was not built at any of the sites investigated!

Cost/Benefit	Site			
	Nuthampstead	**Thurleigh**	**Cublington**	**Foulness**
Third London airport construction	178	166	184	179
Extension/closure of Luton airport	−1	−1	−1	10
Airport services	71	67	75	63
Meteorology	3	2	5	2
Airspace movement	987	972	960	973
Passenger user costs	868	889	887	1041
Freight user costs	17	14	13	23
Road capital	8	3	7	7
Rail capital	8	4	4	16
Air safety	0.5	0.5	0.5	3
Defence	52	73	66	20
Public scientific establishments	11	17	2	3
Private airfields	10	12	9	3
Residential conditions (noise, off site)	19	6	9	4
Residential conditions (on site)	3	2	5	−
Luton noise costs	−	−	−	7
Schools, hospitals and public authority buildings (including noise)	4	5	3	1
Agriculture	7	5	3	4
Commerce and industry (including noise)	1	2	1	0.1
Recreation (including noise)	4	4	7	0.3
Work and service journeys to airport	24	25	26	27
Total net costs (discounted to 1982)	4434	4419	4416	4651
expressed as differences from lowest cost site	18	3	0	235

Figure 17.3 CBA of Sites for Third London Airport

18 *Environmental Impact Assessment (EIA)*

Since July 1988, it has been a legal requirement in the UK for certain large-scale projects, likely to have a significant effect on the environment, to have an EIA carried out before the project is submitted for approval. The emphasis derives from the concept of 'sustainable environments' and is seen as an essential aid to good, rational decision-making. It is closely associated with CBA, but is generally less quantitative and wider in scope and CBA is often used within EIA.

The environment, comprising:

the *abiotic* or lifeless elements, such as land, water or climate; the *biotic* or living elements, such as humans, flora and fauna, and the *social* elements of human behaviour, is seen as something which can beneficially or adversely affect humans. Therefore, the environment must be measured and the effects of the proposals, good and bad, calculated with reference to the different scales involved:

Environmental Impact Analysis

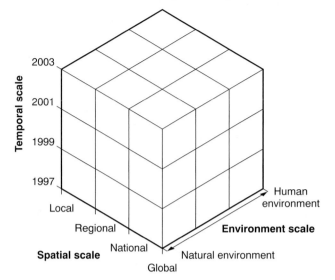

Figure 18.1

- spatial (geographical) scale, from local to global impact

- temporal (time) scale as far into the future as necessary

- environment scale from natural environment to human environment. (Figure 18.1)

An EIA is a balanced appraisal of the potential effects of a major proposal on the physical environment and some aspects of the cultural or human environment, where the emphasis is on reducing the adverse impacts to the minimum. The objective is to find out the magnitude and the significance of individual environmental impacts. Here *impacts* means anything which leads to change in, or affects, an essential element of the environment. These could be:

- physical environmental impacts

- socio-economic or cultural

- direct or indirect

- short-term or long-term

- good or bad

- local or regional or national or international in scale

- reversible or irreversible in effects

- affecting only sections of the population

- quantifiable or qualitative

Method

1 Define the baseline characteristics of the environment under study.

   a Summarize the current environmental situation by listing the main characteristics of the existing environment.

   b Forecast the future of those environmental features if the planned development does *not* take place.

2 Define the proposed development:

- its objectives
- its geographical boundaries
- its main characteristics.

3 Identify the possible impacts of the proposal (from stage 2) both good and bad, on the environment (from stage 1), distinguishing between the *natural environment* (flora, fauna, pollution, soil, ecology, habitats, insects, etc.); and the *human environment* (aesthetic quality, employment in the environment, housing, cultural factors, health, safety, recreation, social well-being, etc.).

4 It often is best to use an *environmental interaction matrix* (Figure 18.2) to identify all the factors that will affect an environment:

   a) Draw a rectangular matrix with the characteristics of the environment identified in stage 1, on the vertical axis and the characteristics of the proposal identified in stage 2, on the horizontal axis.

   b) Shade in the matrix cells where there is an effect, interaction or impact.

Summary Environmental Intersection Matrix

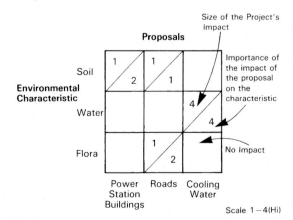

Figure 18.2

5 Identify the cells where there is impact. This is called *scoping*, as it identifies the scope of the really essential environmental issues which have to be addressed and helps to define the limits of your analysis.

6 Use this information to attempt to measure, from the rest of your data, the level of impact.

7 Describe alternatives to the proposals which might reduce adverse impacts and still achieve the objectives sought. This might include:

- alternative sites
- consequences of no action at all
- uncertainties in the proposal
- completely new proposals giving the same benefits
- mitigating measures within the existing proposal: describe modifications to the proposal which might reduce, eliminate or compensate adverse impacts (for example, landscaping an industrial development) and thereby make it more acceptable.
  - specific site or construction changes
  - technical measures, such as pollution controls
  - aesthetic or cosmetic changes, such as mounds of earth or trees
- Identify the unavoidable adverse impacts which might cause irretrievable and irreversible changes.

8 Compare each possible proposal against the original and identify the preferred alternative or preferred modifications, assessing risks and uncertainties. You might want to use separate environmental impact matrices for each possibility.

9 Make decision.

10 Write the EIA report.

Watchpoints on EIA

In Britain, the Department of the Environment, Transport and the Regions insists that EIAs should focus on:

1 *Irreversible effects on the environment from the proposal.*

2 *The costs and benefits to different groups in the population.*

3 *Uncertainties that might change the effects.*

4 *A monetary evaluation of the proposal and its effects.*

1 Good method to focus on the consequences of projects.

2 Should show positive and negative effects, but there is a tendency to concentrate on adverse impacts.

Route of proposal, number of lanes, nature of traffic, landscaping, entry and exit roads, mapped and measured	Is there a need for it? Are there alternatives: other routes, other road possibilities, or other policies?
Does it fit with planning policies, both local and national?	Effects on local road system good and bad
Closeness to residential areas and effects on population and communities	Cost benefit analysis
Effects on noise, air pollution, drainage, aesthetics, soil	Impacts from the construction phase
Safety of pedestrians and vehicles	Implications for railways
Commercial and industrial implications, including financial changes, employment	Social and psychological impacts: health and safety, relocation, impaired lifestyle, accessibility changes, leisure enjoyment
Compulsory purchase of properties on the route	Property value changes, land-use changes
Implications for future traffic patterns and growth	Costings of project and value for money
Energy factors	Hazards and emergency services effects
Environmental protection measures required for flora, fauna, scenery	Effects on existing environmentally sensitive areas and protected areas or features

Figure 18.3 Environmental Factors to be Investigated for Motorway Proposals

3 You have to decide which 'impacts' are 'significant' – which bring the biggest unwanted changes?

4 To some extent, EIA decisions are highly subjective, as no two individuals will view the environment in quite the same way.

5 Can use many of the other decision-making methods described in this book, in its various stages, especially CBA, sieve maps, tables, decision trees and matrices.

6 Aims to identify modifications in order to maximize benefits and minimize environmental costs.

7 Environmental considerations may be outweighed by economic or political considerations in the final decision-making process.

8 Provide maps and appropriate charts, tables and diagrams at each stage.

9 Figure 18.3 lists some of the factors that may need to be addressed in looking at a motorway proposal, showing just how complex an EIA can be.

19 Statistics

The use of statistics can add precision and support to your conclusions, if properly handled. Many texts already exist to teach the methodology of statistics for geographical analyses and the details of individual techniques are not presented here. Use any statistical measure that you consider fruitful and are familiar with in analysing your information in order to reach a decision. Many are contained in computer software packages and the most useful statistics include:

- *Frequency distributions*, with simple counts, percentages, cumulative percentages and totals, perhaps with a table, graph or diagram

- *Descriptive Statistics* take this analysis one step further and give a good, rapid, summary overview as a starter to your analysis:

  - Minimum value
  - Maximum value
  - Mean
  - Mode
  - Median
  - Range
  - Percentiles
  - Variance
  - Standard deviation
  - Nearest Neighbour Analysis

- *Inferential Statistics* can be used to test your ideas and hypotheses, and to analyse the significance of results. They will, however, generally take longer to calculate:

  - Chi-Squared
  - Spearman's Rank Correlation
  - Pearson's Product-Moment Correlation
  - Regression

Watchpoints on Statistics

1 Be sure that you are aware of what any statistical test will show – do not use any if you cannot explain your results from the test!

2 Can be time-consuming, so be sure the test is useful and that you can carry it out quickly.

3 Statistical results are only pointers to, and measures of, relationships; of themselves they do not prove cause and effect – that is where you must add common-sense!

4 Use a technique you are happy with – can you calculate it easily? Do you understand what it really shows you? Will it take too much time? Does it add anything to the decision process?

5 Correlation and Regression show the *nature of the association* between variable sets – they do not, necessarily, even with high levels of significance, show that one variable *causes* the changes in the other variable.

20 Group Decision-Making

Real-life geographical decision-making problems often involve more than one decision-maker, and decision-makers often make their choices with only limited knowledge of what the others will do. Often there are many conflicting influences from politicians, businessmen and interest groups and each may have differing aims and differing abilities to attain these aims.

It is hard for a single decision-maker to understand all of the complex interrelatedness in such a scenario. Outside of the examination room, the use of a group of decision-makers has much to commend it, the synergy of the group (the whole is greater than the parts) is important:

- A wider information base is used with more than one mind of knowledge and experience bearing on the problem.

- A group of different individuals, each with different viewpoints and personalities, may identify far more elements to a problem than a single person (Figure 20.1).

- Bias, assumptions and prejudice are reduced as extreme views are moderated by the group.

- Problems always seem easier when shared and there is safety in numbers! (Figure 20.2). The ideal is for the wide variety of viewpoints and

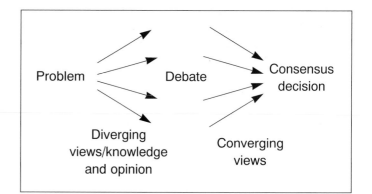

Figure 20.2 The Ideal Group Method

opinions represented by the group, which *diverge*, to be debated until they begin to *converge* on a consensus decision.

- Group decision-making can quickly increase the individual's experience and therefore future personal effectiveness in decision-making.

- Decisions can carry more weight, or be more authoritative if they come as an agreed decision by a group, particularly if the group is large (Figure 20.3).

- Many methods can be employed and most geographical decision-making problems can be adapted for group analysis.

- Groups may understand the issues better and explore more ideas, as they resolve conflicting views in their deliberations.

- Many of the *Mind Mapping* techniques (Section 13) can be used by groups to organize ideas.

Methods

A Informal Group Discussions

This can be as simple as talking through the problem with a friend or informal group. It brings more minds to the problem but a lack of structure makes it difficult to derive a solid benefit. All members must be allowed to freely participate.

B Formal Group Discussions

Some formal structure ensures that no part of the problem is missed and that results are properly worked out and recorded.

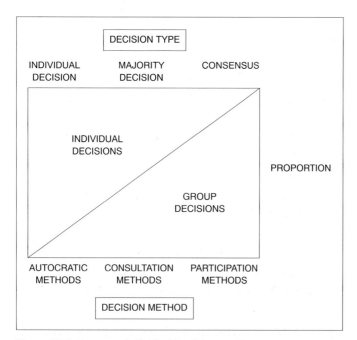

Figure 20.1 Group vs. Individual Decision-making

1 Brainstorming Emphasis is on generating creative ideas in quantity, so all ideas, even if wild and fanciful, are encouraged. Discussion is completely open and the group tries to cover all conceivable possibilities. The emphasis is on generating ideas and these are later modified to eliminate unworkable solutions. There are some basic rules:

- Concentrate on producing ideas and suspend the need to judge the views put forward.

- Relax and let all participants wander at will over the problem, try to keep management of the discussion to a minimum – freewheeling is the key!

- Go for quantity, not quality of inputs.

- Let members modify and improve other's ideas.

- Do not worry, at least to begin with, about the practicalities of the solutions that arise.

- At the end, evaluate the alternatives and make a group decision.

2 Fishbowling The group sits in a circle with one chair in the centre. Each member in turn sits in the middle (of the fishbowl) and presents their own *personal arguments or solutions*. Others may ask questions, but must not discuss or modify the ideas at this stage. The focus is thus, unlike in brainstorming, on extracting purely individual, unmodified views before general discussion begins.

3 Expert Groups The problem is broken down into its elements and small groups are assigned to each element. These 'experts' then study their one aspect in detail and report to the whole group. This can work well, but beware of cliques or over-dominant sub-groups. It is important that each expert group does not lose sight of the whole problem by focusing only on their small portion, a balance must be maintained.

4 Delphi Technique The problem is restated as a series of questions and each member of the group takes these away and submits a written, personal answer to the questions. Copies of all answers, with a summary of the group's overall opinions, are presented again to the group who are then invited to modify or revise their individual ideas in the light of the last round of results. So another, refined, round of answers is produced and the cycle

is repeated as long as necessary, until no real change occurs in the group summary and you have arrived at a consensus. This has been used with groups of experts in predicting global futures.

C Operational Game Role-Playing

Real problems involve decision-makers in trying to predict the actions of others, in trying to get others to support their views and frequently in attempting to influence decisions from a limited resource or knowledge base. Operational gaming provides a means of simulating real decision problems, and role-playing can be an informative and motivating way of dealing with geographical problems. Most decision-making problems in this book can be adapted to be enacted with individuals in the group playing the roles of the participants in the real process.

Groups and Decision 'Authority'

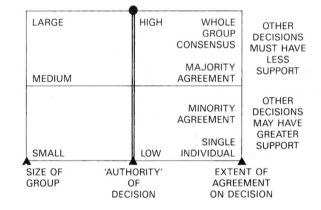

Figure 20.3

Watchpoints on Group Decision-Making

1 Good where there are a variety of factors or wide-ranging data sets to be employed.

2 Ideal for 'satisficer' problems and problems involving chance elements and a range of viewpoints.

3 Role-playing gaming methods are stimulating and can give valuable insights into the complexity of real decision-making, but need all participants to take on their roles and identities with enthusiasm.

4 Aids the identification of key essentials and focuses on processes and values.

5 Game-playing is participatory simulation and a good way of gaining decision-making experience rapidly.

6 Needs time to organize and operate, and it requires commitment of the group to ensure success.

7 Good where there are qualitative factors involved and where empathy may be required for a variety of viewpoints.

8 Best when 'training' for decision-making, as a wide pool of knowledge and experience can be employed in a short space of time and no single individual is isolated or put on the spot.

9 Can be very effective at generating new ideas or viewpoints

10 Group methods can have drawbacks:

- Allocating subsets of the problems to group members or sub-groups can lose sight of the whole problem.

- Individuals may conform to the majority view rather than express contrary ideas (and so impose on themselves a kind of self-censorship).
- There can be a tendency to compromise rather than take bold decisions. Indeed, it may foster indecision.
- Strong personalities, who may not have the best answers, may nevertheless dominate and force the development of what the Americans call 'groupthink' – quick decisions arrived at in order to avoid conflict and argument.
- Smaller groups tend to be more effective.
- Conflict within a group can make it indecisive, but if allowed to produce a consensus decision, can also be extremely productive.
- There can be lack of direction unless properly managed.
- Takes time!

21 Information Technology and Decision-Making

With the increasing availability of computers at home, school and workplace, it is important that you are aware of some of the possible applications of IT to decision-making. Here, we are only presenting a brief survey of some of the options and some of the software available – things change so rapidly that it would be foolish to be too specific. You have access to one of these programs already by purchasing this book, and others may well be found in your school or home. Remember that, for our purposes, you should use them simply to gain experience in decision-making, because they will *not* be available in examinations!

Information Technology can aid decision-making by:

- Reducing the time spent on technical details like calculating statistics
- Reducing the errors in calculations and analysis
- Helping the presentation of decision reports
- Giving access to data, like the census or remote sensing satellite images, which can be difficult to obtain easily
- Opening up new scenarios for decision-making exercises

- Allowing real-time decision-making, when the scenario will change whether or not you make decisions – just like the real world!
- Develop your skills at mapping and other techniques
- Automate a whole decision-making procedure
- Allow you to try out decision-making techniques that would normally take far too long
- Help you to improve your decision-making skills – because if you do not make a good decision the first time, just run the program again
- Make decision-making a lot of fun!

Watchpoints with Information Technology

1 IT can involve considerable expense to obtain the hardware and software.

2 You can be lulled into a false sense of proficiency – in the end, it all has to be done by hand in examinations!

3 Some software can take some time for you to understand enough to use it properly.

4 Remember, the more sophisticated the software, the longer it will take to understand and use – keep as much as possible to the simpler programs, but, if you can access them, by all means try out the others too.

5 The more complex the software, particularly in graphics, the larger and more powerful will be the computer requirements and it may well need a CD ROM facility to run adequately.

Broadly, there are four groups of useful software:

Analysis, Mapping and Presentation Software

There is a vast range of software available to help in your analysis of information, the mapping of results, production of graphs and diagrams, and the presentation of your decision-making report.

Word Processing Software, like *Wordstar* or *Word for Windows*, can improve your presentation, and many have spell checking, some even grammar checking facilities. The whole of the text for this book was produced on a word processor.

Spreadsheet Software, like *Excel, Lotus 1-2-3* or *Supercalc*, can help you to analyse and statistically test your data, produce tables of data and make calculations based on them, using your own formulae or standard statistical formulae (very useful with matrices). All can produce professional looking graphics from the tables of your data, even helping you to select classes and groupings of your data – Bar Charts, Pie Charts, Line Graphs of all kinds, Area Charts, Scatter Graphs, Circular Graphs, Logarithmic Graphs, 2-Dimensional and 3-Dimensional Symbols and Graphs, are all possibilities.

Database Software, like *Access, dBase* or *FoxPro* is slightly more sophisticated and can handle extremely large datasets. All can manipulate numerical and literal (written) data (for example, sorting by alphabetical order), and can be queried (for example, extracting all places with a particular postcode, or all rock field samples between two particular sizes). Many calculations can be made and all programs have excellent presentational capabilities, with many report templates available.

They are particularly good at analysing survey results – for example, from questionnaires or land use surveys. Relational databases like these are at the heart of Geographic Information Systems (GIS).

Mapping Software, like *MapViewer* and *MapInfo*, can be used to produce all kinds of maps and some are capable of quite advanced GIS functions. All require the input of data into tables, from which they can produce maps – they can help to organize data into classes, select shading schemes and import digital base maps. All can be annotated, so producing excellent map presentations. They can draw dot maps, proportional symbol maps and choropleth maps with ease and virtually automatically (once you have selected your data from the table).

The more elaborate can query the maps as simple Geographic Information Systems. *The Microsoft Office package for Windows 95* has incorporated a scaled-down version of the *MapInfo* mapping and GIS software (called DataMap) into its *Excel* Spreadsheet program.

Remote Sensing Software is usually expensive, though *IDRISI* is relatively cheap and is a good basic introduction to the use of satellite imagery, with simple GIS capabilities as well.

Presentation Software, like *Microsoft Publisher* are perhaps less useful, since their prime purpose is to produce graphic designs or slides for presentations, though desk top publishing programs (DTP) can be useful if you are proficient with computers and have enough time to devote to them.

Specific Data Software is built around its database. *SCAMP-2 (Schools Census Analysis and Mapping Package)* is a complete version of the 1991 Census for England and Wales, and comes with *MAP91*, a simple mapping and GIS program which can undertake quite sophisticated analysis of the census information and cartographic presentation. (See Exercise 28.) SCAMP-2 can create many kinds of maps, using data down to Ward and Enumeration District levels, and can produce detailed analyses, both graphical and statistical. It includes all boundary data so that you can produce analyses and maps of any part of England or Wales, uses O.S grid references and has an extensive set of symbol and feature databases (including Roads, Rivers, National Parks, Houses and Gardens and Places of Interest). Help is given with classification of data and shading of maps and it can produce choropleth maps, proportional symbol maps and dot maps.

Decision-Making Software

There are many programs on the market which will undertake particular decision-making procedures for you. They tend to be expensive, but are worth a look if you have access to them.

Project Management Software, like *Microsoft Project*, is often very sophisticated and will automate the processes for Decision Trees, Gannt Charts, PERT Charts, Critical Path Analysis and Cost Benefit Analysis, in particular. All can produce excellent reports and graphics.

Route-Finding Software, like *Autoroute*, uses most of the forms of *Route-Finding CPA* detailed elsewhere in this book and can show you how complex problems can be solved – though it is difficult with most to understand exactly how it arrives at its decisions!

Specific Technique Software *STRAD* is a specific decision-making technique program produced by STRADSPAN of Sheffield and is an excellent computerisation of *Strategic Choice* and *Analysis of Interrelated Decision Areas* that are presented elsewhere in this book. It includes many example scenarios and enables many approaches to solving development and planning problems to be tried.

Geographical Information Systems (GIS)

A GIS is a computerised system that uses geo-referenced (that is, located) information databases, just like a map, but which is capable of holding vast data sets that can be:

- Linked together by common *geo-referencing*. GIS uses geography (location) as the common key and, strictly speaking, geographic features can be located with:
  - *relative location referencing*, such as street addresses, postal code area or telephone code area. These rely on use of a key map to show where areas are in relation to each other and cannot show unique, absolute locations.
  - *geo-referencing or geo-coding*, which uses absolute location by coordinates. These can be simple x,y coordinates, grid references or latitude/longitude and have the advantage of giving precise, unique and unambiguous locations for all features – they are therefore used in GIS.

- Every *feature* has a *geo-referenced location* and its own set of *attributes* (details held in a table in a database)
- So, every feature or every location can be looked at in detail from the database, using the common *geo-referenced database* location points to match up the elements in the detailed *attribute databases* (Figure 21.1)
- All this detail, on all of the features or locations, can be combined so you can use them to make maps of all kinds of distributions, or process the geographical information by asking questions.
  - *spatial queries*, like, 'how many people live at locations within 50 metres of a school?', or, 'how much green space will be taken up by this road proposal?', or, 'what is the shortest route between all towns of over 50 000 people?'. All these questions require the use of precise location information.
  - *aspatial* (non-locational) *queries*, like, 'what is the average population in these towns?'. Such questions do not need to have precise location information.
- Visualize each of your data sets as maps of your area (say for population, housing, land use, roads, administrative areas, schools and opinion survey results, as in Figure 21.1). In GIS these maps are known as *coverages*.
- Now overlay the maps – every point in the area can be geo-referenced through all of the data maps or coverages and then we can look up the details in the attribute databases.
- In our example, point 'A' might have:
  - young people of Caribbean origin with high educational attainment and 3 person households
  - living in semi-detached houses with parking
  - within a residential area
  - within 10 metres of a main road, which has heavy traffic flows and pollution and accidents at the nearby junction
  - in administrative area Y
  - within 50 metres of a secondary school
  - and people in that area generally voted 'yes' to a survey on building a new road in the area!
- Now imagine that you have hundreds or even thousands of geo-referenced data maps, each with an extensive attribute database linked to it to give detailed information – now you have a GIS!

G I S Relational Databases

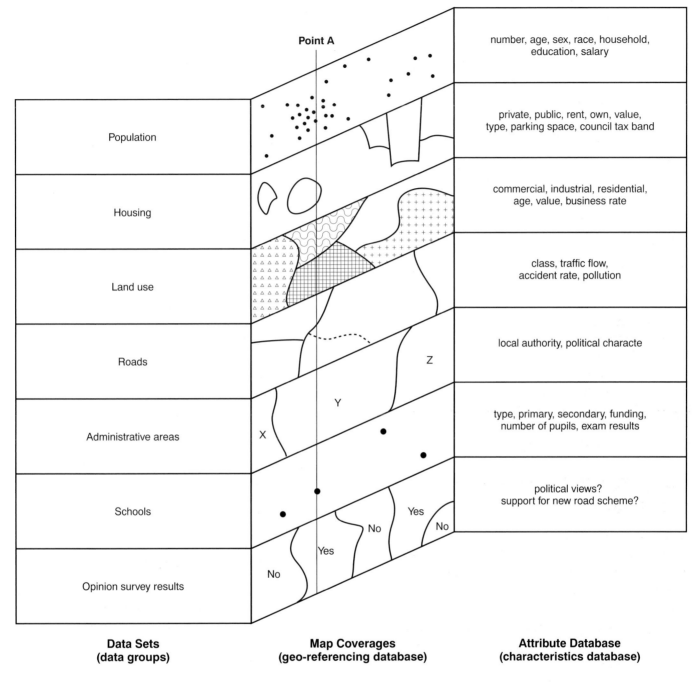

Figure 21.1

- You can ask questions framed as:
  - what is at point x?
  - where are all the places with x and y and z?
  - what features are within x metres of y?
  - what has changed over time x?
  - what spatial patterns exist?
  - what if we …?

Watchpoints on GIS

1 Powerful decision-making tool, but:

- requires a relatively sophisticated computer system and program
- needs time to become proficient in its use
- not suitable for examinations
- can be expensive.

2 Common systems include full GIS systems like *ARC/INFO* and mapping packages with some GIS capabilities like *MAPINFO*. A scaled-down version of *MAPINFO* is included in the Microsoft spreadsheet program *EXCEL* in the Windows 95 version of *Microsoft Office*, and gives a good general, accessible, introduction to GIS.

3 Deals with spatial relationships – the heart of Geography!

4 It has been estimated that anything up to about 85% of all data being processed globally has an inherent locational element, even if it is only an address or postcode – just think of the potential uses for a GIS!

5 Uses common geographical topology – points, lines, polygons (areas) and surfaces to represent distributions.

6 Is a sophisticated spatial relational database, not a mapping technique as such, and is best described as 'a system using a spatial database to answer queries of a geographical (locational) nature'.

Computer Simulation Games

Computer games become ever more sophisticated and ever more graphically complex. As well as being great fun to play, many are aids to educational understanding and decision-making. Many, particularly race, flight simulator and warfare games, present geographical landscapes and these are becoming more realistic and authentic all the time. Dramatic scenery can enhance the pleasure of a game, but is also instructive, and can incorporate true-video sequences. In many, the player can alter or create landscapes. (See Exercise 33 for more details about *SimCity 2000*, the game that allows you to plan an entire city).

22 *Evaluation of Sources*

In a Court of Law, it is important that those who make the decision about the accused use information that is as relevant, important and accurate as possible, so that they arrive at a fair verdict. So it is with geographical decision-making – some of the material we use to arrive at our decision may be misleading, some may be inaccurate, some may be irrelevant. We need methods to *evaluate* our sources, so that we can sift out the worthless and be confident of the decisions we make.

Remember, however sophisticated the techniques of analysis you have used on your information, if the information itself is flawed, then your decisions may be worthless.

Method

Questions we need to apply to each of our source materials:

1 Is the information important to our enquiry? Does it focus on our problem?

2 Is it relevant to our decision?

3 Is it useful?

4 Is it valid?

5 What are its advantages if we use it?

6 What are its disadvantages if we use it?

7 What are its limitations?

8 Does it contain a bias?

9 Who was the author of the source? Are they reliable?

10 Is it comprehensive, or does it have missing elements?

11 What was the original purpose of the source material?

12 When was the material collected? Do you know anything about that period that could be useful background?

13 Is it corroborated or substantiated (supported) by any of our other sources, or do they conflict?

The answers to these questions depend on the kind of source information you are using, and, particularly, whether it is a:

• Primary or Secondary source

• Written published source, and whether a:

- Private source
- Public source

- Graphical or map source

A Primary and Secondary sources

Primary Sources are sources beyond which it is impossible to go – for example, your own questionnaire survey or land use mapping. The category can be stretched to include sources which are not first hand, but that are 'raw', in the sense that no-one has modified them, manipulated them, interpreted them, or otherwise introduced any kind of bias to them. So, an aerial photograph could, legitimately, be considered to be a primary source, even though you did not collect it yourself. They are often unpublished. So, someone's personal diary from the 18th century would be an unpublished primary source, though a modern author's discussion of that diary would not.

Secondary sources are sources beyond which it is possible to go. For example, the modern author's analysis of the 18th century diary – you could go back to the original diaries and avoid modern bias. The material is generally collected by someone else and generally published. A book, for example, is a collection of material that has been organized and interpreted by the author to present a particular perspective, and that is where bias may be introduced. They are often the only kind presented in a decision-making exercise, and are considered to be generally less valuable than primary sources because the writer, compiler or map-maker will have introduced their own interpretations, selections and biasses to the material.

B Written Published Sources

1 *Private Written Published Sources.* These include books, articles, sets of data and reports that do *not* originate from some official body. They are therefore considered to be more difficult to evaluate than official written sources because we generally have information on how, why and when official data was collected and we rarely have this for private sources. Ask yourself:

- Who wrote it? Can they be trusted? Were they experts in their area?
- Is it authentic?
- What sources did they use?

- Can you corroborate it (match it to your other data)?
- Never assume that because something was published it must be correct or valid
- What was the purpose of the source?
- Do you know anything about the background, the period or the area in the source that may help?

A 19th century *Town Directory* (see Exercise 26), for example, will probably have a description of the town's history, its main buildings, its markets, charities and local villages. Then it will list inhabitants and businesses, by occupation and possibly by street address. However, you will notice that it only lists the 'important' people and rarely has any entries for the labouring people – it is therefore biassed and limited, but how do we understand and use it?

The key is in its purpose – directories were produced as a commercial product to sell, therefore they included only those who might buy it, who paid to be in it, or who needed it for business. As long as we evaluate and understand the limitations, we can use the source material.

Our examples (Figures 22.1 and 22.2) both relate to the town of Caen in Normandy. Figure 22.1 is an extract from the Michelin Guide, it stresses history in a particular way, specifically to attract the tourist visitor and to give a quick potted viewpoint. Figure 22.2 is written by the Mayor of Caen to commemorate the 40th anniversary, in 1984, of the D-Day landings in Normandy (in 1944, that town was virtually obliterated). This text too, is aimed at visitors, but has an entirely different viewpoint.

2 *Official Written Published Sources.* These are generally easier to evaluate, since they usually come with much information on the methods of data collection, the categories used and the purpose of the survey. They are different because:

- Official bodies usually have strict, known rules for gathering information
- They have financial resources to do possibly thorough surveys
- They are likely to be repeated or revised at intervals
- Like the census, they may be enforcible by law and therefore comprehensive
- Again, like the census, anonymity is often assured and so responses may be more valid

CAEN***

Caen, capital of Lower Normandy, Prefecture of the Calvados Region, an industrial centre and river port, is a large bustling city. A cultural centre as well, it is an attractive town with houses built in Caen stone, beautiful abbeys and churches, and fine modern buildings.

HISTORICAL NOTES

William the Bastard and Proud Matilda. – Caen developed from the island at the confluence of the Orne and Odon Rivers which was fortified very early by the Normans but only grew in importance in the 11C. Then it became the favourite town of Duke William who was to leave his imprint on it for all time.

After his victory at Val-es-Dunes over the rebel barons of the Cotentin and Bessin Regions, William, now assured in his own Duchy, demanded the hand in marriage of Matilda of Flanders. The Duke's cousin was not flattered at his proposal: 'I would rather take the veil than be wed to a bastard,' she replied. The Duke swallowed the insult, but later, mad with rage and love, rode straight to Lille and forced his way into the palace of the Count of Flanders. According to the Chronicler of Tours, he seized Matilda by her plaits, dragged her round the room, kicked her fiercely and, leaving her gasping for breath, rode off at full gallop.

Matilda, beaten, consented to marry the Duke and the marriage was celebrated in spite of the opposition of the Pope who objected to the cousins' distant kinship. In 1059, Lanfranc had the excommunication, which weighed heavily upon the Duke, lifted. William and Matilda, in penance, founded two abbeys – the Abbey aux Hommes and the Abbaye aux Dames, making Caen virtually a Benedictine city – and four hospitals.

When William left for England, the faithful Matilda assumed the regency of the Duchy of Normandy. Two years later, in 1068, she was crowned Queen of England at Westminster. When she died, in 1083, she was buried in the Abbaye aux Dames.

The Caen Battle. – The battle lasted for more than two months. Bombs poured down on 6 June 1944; fire raged for eleven days and the central area was burnt out. On 9 July the Canadians who had taken Carpiquet Airport, entered the town from the west, but the Germans who had fallen back to Vaucelles began to shell it in their turn. Throughout the battle the citizens of Caen sought refuge in their famous buildings: 1500 camped out in the Abbaye aux Hommes; the Malhenbe Lycée refectory was used as a hospital and the dead were buried in its courtyards: the Good Saviour Hospice sheltered 4000. The Allies were informed through the Resistance and the buildings were not bombed. The largest shelter was provided in the Fleury Quarry a mine south of the town where families remained in the underground passages until the end of July.

The final liberation ceremony took place at Vaucelles on 20 July, although another month was to pass before the last German shell had fallen on Caen.

CAEN'S EXPANSION

A New Town. – The destroyed central area has been entirely rebuilt since 1944, the St-Pierre and St-Jean Churches, the Abbeys (Hommes and Dames) being safeguarded and the castle being cleared of disfiguring surroundings.

The new university which has been erected north of the castle, now also includes a hospital. New quarters continue to grow on the outskirts of the city and a large industrial zone takes up 500 ha – 1482 acres south of the city. Construction of a nuclear centre has recently been completed. The town, which is more open than it was, retains contact with the country through the Prairie, a wide area of greenery which juts deeply into the town.

Caen's Steel Industry. – Caen is the natural outlet for the iron ore mines of Lower Normandy which, with an annual production of 1 million tons (the grades of ore being about 45%), are the second largest in France. This mineral wealth encouraged the establishment of heavy industry on a considerable scale locally just before the First World War.

The works and surrounding town of Mondeville-Colombelles were destroyed in 1944 and have since been rebuilt on modern lines. Production capacity is now more than 1 million tons of steel a year.

The Seaport of Caen. – While it is the Orne that has made Caen a seaport since the beginning of time, it is Baron Cachin who, in the middle of the 19C. gave Caen its true seaport character. To link the town with the sea he had a canal nearly 12 km – 6 miles long dug parallel with the Orne constructed a series of locks along it and converted Ouistreham into an outer port. Since it was first constructed, work has never ceased on the canal, deepening and widening it and adding new basins to keep pace with the requirements of the ever expanding steel industry. Today the port of Caen with an annual traffic of nearly 2 million tons has four main docks and a new dock 564 m – 1861 ft in length in Blainville.

Two locks have been built at Ouistreham, and the sea channel deepened so that barges of up to 16000 tons loaded with ore and ships of up to 28000 tons are able to sail up to Caen.

Figure 22.1

6th JUNE 1944 # THE BATTLE OF CAEN
40th ANNIVERSARY 6th JUNE 1984

"The Anvil of Victory"

Such is the title of the English version of the book which, twenty years ago, the historian Alexander MAC KEE devoted to the BATTLE OF CAEN which started on the 6th June 1944 with the Allied Landings, followed by the liberation of the City on the 9th and 19th July and concluded on the 22nd August at Chambois by the defeat of the German armies engaged in the region.

THE ANVIL OF VICTORY

Over and above the incontestable fact which it evokes concerning the historical part which our city played at the time, the gripping title of Alexander MAC KEE is profoundly true.

THE ANVIL – Yes, because Caen and its inhabitants found themselves suddenly at the crux of the Anglo-Canadian plan whose aim was to attract and keep occupied the greatest possible number of Germ Divisions in order to help the Americans to by-pass Lower Normandy by the South. And, this being so, the city suffered for weeks batterings, attacks, ruin, fire, tears, blood and death. Does not the great French dictionary LAROUSSE define the work "anvil" as "an object destined to receive a shock?".

THE ANVIL OF VICTORY – Yes, again, because the Battle of Caen allowed the Allies to win the Battle of Normandy by encircling the German armies and then liberating in less than 3 months the rest of the French territory with the exception of two "Départements", in liaison with the armies which landed in Provence on the 15th August 1944.

The Allied landing and the Battle of Normandy which pivoted on Caen were carried out in extraordinarily difficult conditions, so obstinate was the German resistance. The greatest military operation of all time mobilised 3 000 000 men (Americans, British, Canadian, French, Polish, Belgians, Checkoslovakians and Germans) and cost 600 000 men killed or wounded. 15000 civilians were killed.

Like so many other towns and villages in our region, the City of Caen, 40 years ago, played its historical part in the re-conquest of liberty; its ruin and the death of several thousands of its inhabitants are eternal witnesses.

The extraordinary will of the survivors was instrumental in our City arising magnificently from the rubble and becoming what it is today. That can never be repeated too often.

Today, the sacrifice of 1944 keeps all its sense, and one must not hesitate to say to the rising generations, more generally to those who, not having known the Battle of Caen, ask: "WHY DID IT HAPPEN AND WHAT USE WAS IT?".

The reply to this ardent question is this: the Second World War (1939–1945) was not a war of peoples and of frontiers. It was a gigantic fight of liberty-loving peoples, always menaced and sometimes subdued, against the Fascist ideology, particularly incarnated by Adolf Hitler and Nazi Germany. The sacrifice of Caen in 1944 is placed at a decisive moment in this combat in which France, thanks to all fighters of the Resistance, of Free France and of the French Forces formed in North Africa, and her Allies, they also fighters for Liberty, would emerge victorious.

The reminder of this combat, which must not be a praise of war, is accompanied by an essential lesson, the misunderstanding or forgetting of which could be mortal: **The reasons which made yesterday's combat necessary are still present. Totalitarian ideology constantly menaces the peoples of the earth and the number of democracies is constantly decreasing. It isn't sufficient for a free people to be and to state that it is a democracy to be thus assured of survival. Democracy always needs the active support of those who live it, as oppression is constantly on the watch here and there, inside or outside.**

In this respect, the Second World War takes a large place in the troubled history of liberties.

This message, which should be a basic subject of reflection for our younger co-citizens who are taking part already in the shaping of tomorrow, will soon be spread by the Memorial Museum of the Battle of Normandy which will start to be built in 1985.

Thus, over the coming years, citizens both male and female of all the Nations of the World will follow each other to Caen, the Mecca of contemporary history. May they come to share the firm opinion that a people can only be a people if it is free, that an individual can only be an individual if he or she is free. May they also participate in removing completely and definitively the antagonism between camps which opposed each other in days gone by and who oppose each other still.

"All sons of God!" – this was written by an inspired hand somewhere on the Norman soil where thousands of soldiers faced each other; a hand which, embracing in the same invocation all the fighting men, whatever their nationality, buried in the same earth, the earth which brings them together, – ours!

This will be Caen's honour, after having payed so dearly the price of liberty, to pass on to the world the universal message of Liberty and Fraternity.

Jean-Marie GIRAULT,
Mayor of Caen.

Figure 22.2

The *Sanitary Reports to the General Board of Health* produced in the middle of the 19th century (see Exercise 26) described the town and its inhabitants, with an emphasis on the poor people and their wretched living conditions. It omitted most of the better-off areas and people and was therefore also biassed and selective. How do we understand it?

Again, the key is in the purpose and period of the sources. The Reports were part of the 19th century agitation to develop Public Health legislation in towns – so, we might expect them to highlight, perhaps dramatically, all that was bad about a town.

C Graphical or Mapped Sources

Maps are simplified two-dimensional representations of complex 3-dimensional reality. They therefore have to be *selective* of data and will use particular *graphical methods* to portray their information – we need to know about both in order to evaluate them.

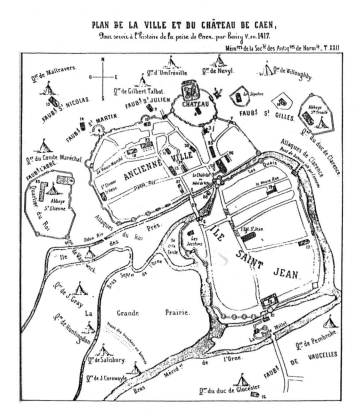

Figure 22.3

- Read its *marginal information* – this may give the title, the name of the compiler, date of survey and date of publication (which can be years apart), the subject, the location, the scale, the key to symbols, the orientation and perhaps a key to adjacent sheets

- Dates are important:
  - the survey date shows when the material was current, not the publication date
  - revision dates may be partial – for example, it was common in the 19th century to simply revise railways on maps, as it was expensive to revise the whole copper plate, so the 'picture' it shows is drawn from more than one period
  - early maps were reprinted many times
  - in general, the older the map, the more we should be wary as techniques were more primitive

- Background is important too – what kind of methods did they use to collect and present information? Was the area difficult to survey (perhaps there was a war in the area)?

- What was the purpose of the map? For example, wartime maps were often biased in order to present a particular viewpoint, traveller's maps like the Ogilby maps would be accurate on information along roads for their users, but less so for areas away from the routes. Cadastral maps (showing ownership boundaries) were likely to be accurate on the boundaries of properties as ownership, and therefore money, was at stake.

- Do you have another map, probably a more recent one, of which you can be more confident? If so, then compare features (and check whether any features are omitted), distances between obvious points and other aspects to see if the other source measures up.

Our two examples (Figures 22.3 and 22.4) are also about the town of Caen in Normandy. Figure 22.3 is a map which has a date of 1417 at the top and relates to the siege of the town in that year by the English King Henry V. It is complete with named military camps around the town set up by the English, but it is not all it seems – it does not really 'look' like a map nearly 700 years old. Look carefully at the top right of the map – you will see a reference to the Society of Antiquaries of Normandy – it is a modern map produced to

Figure 22.4

illustrate the historic event, not a 15th century map, which would have looked very different.

Figure 22.4 is an extract from the Evening Standard of 6 June 1944, D-Day. It presents a particularly up-beat report of the first day's fighting in France – and, as you might expect at such a crucial time, is entirely over-optimistic about

progress in order to keep morale high among troops and the population at home (it took the Allies three months to take Caen).

When you have evaluated your sources as far as you can, use them within the limits you now know that they have and qualify your conclusions if you are uncertain about their true worth.

23 | Remote Sensing: Aerial and Satellite Photographs

You might well be given an aerial photograph or satellite photograph as part of a DME and you need to know how to use and interpret these sources.

Aerial photographs, taken from an aircraft, are more common, since they cover smaller areas at larger scales (and are therefore, closer to our

normal experience of physical and human features), are cheaper to buy, more plentiful, more available and generally easier to interpret. *Satellite images* cover often very large areas of the globe and are more difficult to interpret. They are therefore less likely to show material suitable for a DME.

You are most likely to have a panchromatic (black and white) aerial photograph, which shows differences by change of tone between the extremes of black and white. You may have:

- A *vertical image*, taken with the camera exactly pointing to the ground. This looks like a rectangular plan or map and allows measurement and map drawing from the image. (Figure 23.1i)

- An *oblique image*, with the camera at an angle with the ground. This shows part of the side view of features (which, because it is more usual to us, can be easier to interpret) but is harder to measure from or make maps and can hide detail behind dominant features. (Figure 23.1i). Distortion increases as the angle to the vertical increases and more of a perspective view is given (that is so also for the edges of vertical images).

- A *Stereo Pair*, that is, two photos taken after one another on the flight path (Figure 23.1ii), such that part of each one overlaps. As you have two slightly different views of the same objects you can use a stereoscope to show the image in 3-dimensions (even closer to our usual view of objects!).

The general method of interpretation is, however, similar for both aerial and satellite sources. They are very useful sources because they show everything that was in the shot at the time, without exception. They are not selective like maps, nor are they biased by a compiler or writer.

Aerial Photographs

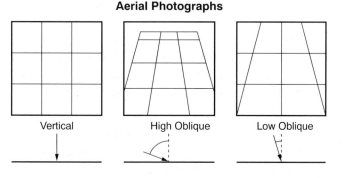

Figure 23.1i

Method

1 Basic rules:

- Work from general patterns to specific features (e.g. identify residential districts before trying to identify a kind of house)
- Work from obvious, known features to unknown features (identify the ones that are easy first!)
- If you cannot be certain, qualify your conclusions, do not be over-confident, give several possible explanations
- Use as much corroborating evidence as you can (e.g. maps of the same area)

2 General aids:

- Read the *border information* on the image to try to home in on the part of the world and the date and time of day it was taken. Note the focal length of the camera used and the altitude of the aircraft.

3 Calculate the scale by:

- Measuring a specific distance on the image and on a map with a known scale
- Calculating the *Representative Fraction* using the formula:
$$\frac{focal\ length}{altitude}$$
- From the sizes of known objects (e.g. cricket pitch)

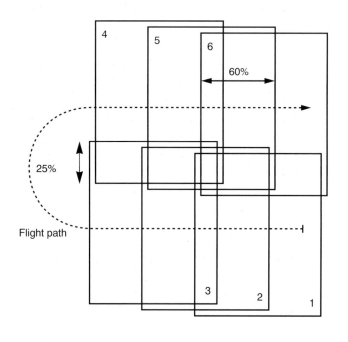

Figure 23.1ii

4 *Orientate* the photo (it can be taken in any direction, north is not necessarily at the top).

- Locate an obvious object on the photo and the same object on a map of which you know the orientation
- In the northern hemisphere temperate region, shadows at midday generally fall north-east to north-west (most photos are taken around midday because that gives the best light and fewer shadows)
- Older Christian churches tend to have their long axis aligned approximately east to west

5 Examine the details.

- Look at the *shape, size and form* of the object
- Use *shadows* to add a kind of side-view to the information
- *Colour or tone* depends on the object's colour, nature of its surface (smooth is more reflective of light), the time of day (at midday the sun is overhead) and weather conditions
- Look at *associated features*, that is, what is around the object (a school might have a playground and games areas marked out, railways have stations, roads do not)
- Make a *sketch map* of the area from the image, using a grid of squares if you have time
- Try to identify the processes creating *physical features*, look for:
  - relief features
  - topography
  - surface cover and vegetation
  - hydrographic features
  - erosion/deposition

Figure 23.2 is an aerial photograph of the town of Dartford in Kent. The border information tells us:

- Reference number 0072 of flight run 540/RAF/1081 DOE
- Photograph taken on 23 February 1953 at 11.20 a.m.
- Focal Length of Camera 6 inches
- Altitude of aircraft 2,500 feet

Using the formula above, we can deduce that the scale is 1:5000. It was taken by the Royal Air Force on 23 February 1953, close to midday. Four features are marked, see if you can identify them before reading further!

- *Feature 1* is apparently within a largely residential area and is large, irregularly shaped with a boundary line and a diagonal straight line.

It has small very white objects in it, some in lines and some darker spotty areas, some of which have white objects inside them.

This is a cemetery – the white objects are gravestones (many are of crystalline and white stone – very reflective), the diagonal and perimeter are paths (smaller than the roads) and the dark spots are trees. Remember the date: 23 February, this is mid-winter, and deciduous trees are without leaves, so you will see 'through' them (you can even see some of the white dots within them)!

- *Feature 2* has a sinewy path and a very square object with a bright line around it and a small building at one end. Further round there is a crescent-shaped object with dark bits at its ends, but it is otherwise very white.

These are a bowling green and a paddling pool. The green is characteristically square, with a gravel path (hence very reflective and white) around it and a clubhouse. The paddling pool is shallow, especially at the centre, so you see more of the reflective concrete base there, the water is deeper at the ends and so darker. Both objects are associated with a park around them (geometric shaped paths, regular flower beds), a common location.

- *Feature 3* is in a commercial/residential zone and is a very large building with a strange shape, like a tent, and faces the road junction on which it stands. It is very much larger than surrounding buildings.

This is a cinema – as the object is near the edge of the vertical photo, you get a slightly more oblique side view and the display hoardings can be seen clearly. The shape is determined by the 'auditorium' design of cinemas and the roof is bright because it is corrugated asbestos which is crystalline and reflects light.

- *Feature 4* is in a residential area, close to a lake and on a main road junction, it is quite large, 'L' shaped and very white. Perhaps it is a large office block?

In fact this was an office complex (for the DHSS), but in reality it was a one-storey, low prefabricated structure and only appears large because, again, it had a white corrugated asbestos roof which looks much larger than it really was. Do not be misled, remember, this is a photograph, so what you see is the result of the reflection of light and this can be difficult to interpret.

Figure 23.2

Watchpoints on Remote Sensing

1 They provide records of physical processes.

2 Over a period of time sequences track changes.

3 They are taken from a viewpoint above the objects and this angle is not normal for us.

4 Complex features can be very difficult to decipher.

5 They may obscure other features.

6 Can show activities in action, for example, traffic on roads and animals in fields – information well in excess of that normally shown on maps.

7 Vegetation can help and hinder:
- Shadows in growing crops can show hidden features (poorer growth over buildings, better over old waste pits)
- Vegetation can hide or obscure detail

8 They rely heavily on your own knowledge of geographical features for proper interpretation.

PART THREE

PRACTICE – GEOGRAPHICAL DECISION-MAKING EXERCISES

24 *Air Pollution and Residential Location*

Decision-Making Exercise

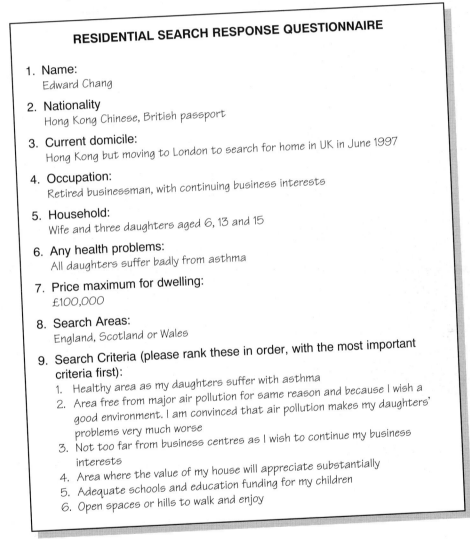

RESIDENTIAL SEARCH RESPONSE QUESTIONNAIRE

1. **Name:**
   Edward Chang

2. **Nationality**
   Hong Kong Chinese, British passport

3. **Current domicile:**
   Hong Kong but moving to London to search for home in UK in June 1997

4. **Occupation:**
   Retired businessman, with continuing business interests

5. **Household:**
   Wife and three daughters aged 6, 13 and 15

6. **Any health problems:**
   All daughters suffer badly from asthma

7. **Price maximum for dwelling:**
   £100,000

8. **Search Areas:**
   England, Scotland or Wales

9. **Search Criteria (please rank these in order, with the most important criteria first):**
   1. Healthy area as my daughters suffer with asthma
   2. Area free from major air pollution for same reason and because I wish a good environment. I am convinced that air pollution makes my daughters' problems very much worse
   3. Not too far from business centres as I wish to continue my business interests
   4. Area where the value of my house will appreciate substantially
   5. Adequate schools and education funding for my children
   6. Open spaces or hills to walk and enjoy

In this scenario, you are asked to assume the role of a consultant working for International Residential Search Inc. (IRS), a company which specializes in finding suitable areas for wealthy clients who wish to move to a new country.

IRS issue a 'Residential Search Response Questionnaire' to their clients and pass the completed questionnaire to one of their consultants in the appropriate country. The consultant then produces a detailed report of possible areas for the new home, based on the criteria identified by the client.

You have been sent a large package from IRS, which includes the response of Edward Chang (above), who left Hong Kong shortly before it was handed back to China on 1 July 1997. You have also been given a variety of maps, tables and other information to help you in making a decision on Mr Chang's behalf. Additionally, you should use your own knowledge of the geography of the United Kingdom. Your report should:

1 Identify, map and explain in detail the selection of those parts of the country which:

- would most ideally suit him and his family
- he should avoid completely in his search.

2 Explain the information you have used in coming to these selections, mapped where necessary.

3 Present 'caveats' (warnings or provisos) to protect the company from any future claims, based on any problems you have identified in evaluating the data you have used.

4 Mr Chang identified the possible links between air pollution and asthma in his criteria. Briefly give your own interpretation of these links, based solely on the information presented here.

Figure 24.2 Standard Regions

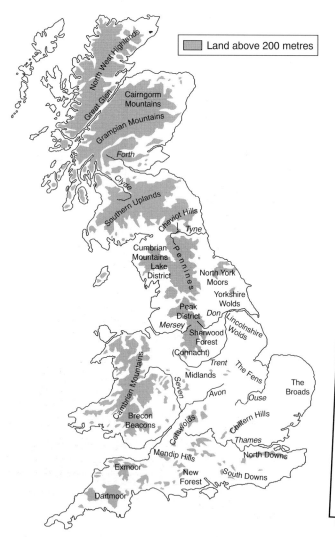

Figure 24.1 Physical Features

PERCENTAGE OF REGIONS AS DESIGNATED AREAS 1996

	National Parks	AONB
North	23	15
Yorks/Humber	20	2
E Midlands	6	3
E Anglia	0	7
South East	0	24
South West	7	27
W Midlands	2	10
North West	1	11
Wales	19	4
Scotland	n/a	13

(Percentage of area of region)
AONB = Areas of Outstanding Natural Beauty

Figure 24.3

Population Density 1991

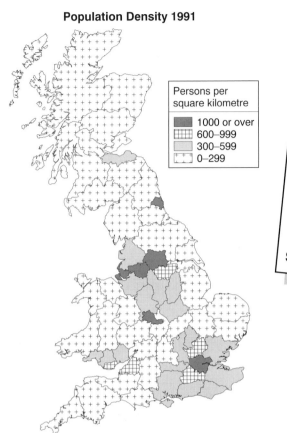

Persons per square kilometre
- 1000 or over
- 600–999
- 300–599
- 0–299

Figure 24.4 Population

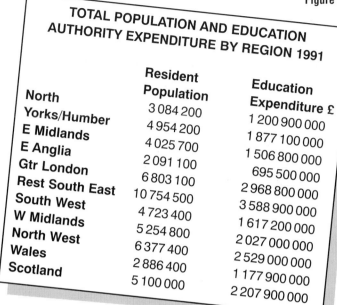

Figure 24.7

TOTAL POPULATION AND EDUCATION AUTHORITY EXPENDITURE BY REGION 1991

	Resident Population	Education Expenditure £
North	3 084 200	1 200 900 000
Yorks/Humber	4 954 200	1 877 100 000
E Midlands	4 025 700	1 506 800 000
E Anglia	2 091 100	695 500 000
Gtr London	6 803 100	2 968 800 000
Rest South East	10 754 500	3 588 900 000
South West	4 723 400	1 617 200 000
W Midlands	5 254 800	2 027 000 000
North West	6 377 400	2 529 000 000
Wales	2 886 400	1 177 900 000
Scotland	5 100 000	2 207 900 000

Nitrogen Dioxide 1993 Average Concentrations

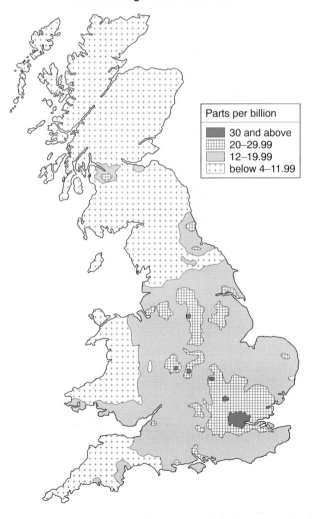

Parts per billion
- 30 and above
- 20–29.99
- 12–19.99
- below 4–11.99

Figure 24.6 Nitrogen Dioxide

Nitrogen Dioxide: NO_2

- 50% from road vehicles (up to 75% in urban areas), the rest from power stations and industry
- Nitrogen oxides, of which nitrogen dioxide is the most important, are a product of fossil fuel combustion and oxidisation
- Affects respiratory disorders and particularly asthmatics and children
- Especially a problem in urban areas and rush hours
- Higher levels in winter
- Produces ozone from the action of sunlight on the gas
- Responsible for 30% of acid deposition in

Figure 24.5

- Britain introduced the Clean Air Act in 1956

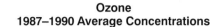

Ozone
1987–1990 Average Concentrations

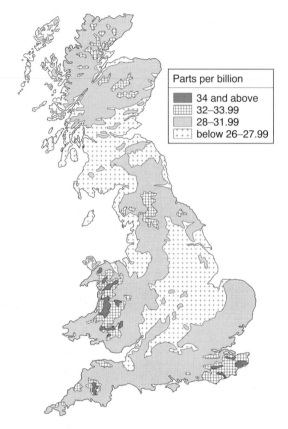

Parts per billion

▓	34 and above
▦	32–33.99
░	28–31.99
⁺	below 26–27.99

Figure 24.8 Ozone

Ozone: O₃

- A form of oxygen that protects the earth from UV rays from the sun when it is in the upper atmosphere 'ozone layer'
- Ground level ozone is an irritant of eyes, nose and respiratory tracts, and a major asthma pollutant
- A product of chemical changes due to the action of sunlight (photochemical) on nitrogen dioxide and hydrocarbons
- A dangerous pollutant in smog conditions
- A potent oxidising agent affecting crops, plants and trees
- Higher levels in day time, in summer, at high temperatures, in temperature inversions and high pressure systems with low wind speeds
- Chemical and atmospheric processes make it a pollutant of the non-urban areas
- May be more persistent in the countryside where the side-effects of vehicular traffic do not disperse the ozone (urban pollution removes ozone!)

Figure 24.9

- On 13 December 1991, 160 people died in London as a result of poor air quality caused by nitrogen dioxide and cold, still weather conditions

Sulphur Dioxide: SO₂

- Up to 72% from power stations, especially coal-fired and oil-fired, the rest from industry, some from diesel vehicles
- Affects respiratory disorders, including asthma
- Higher levels in winter
- The major contributor to acid rain, affecting ecosystems
- A product of the combustion of fossil fuels and oxidisation

Figure 24.10

Sulphur Dioxide
Highest Power Station Emissions 1993

Figure 24.11 Sulphur Dioxide

Air Quality Problems 1988

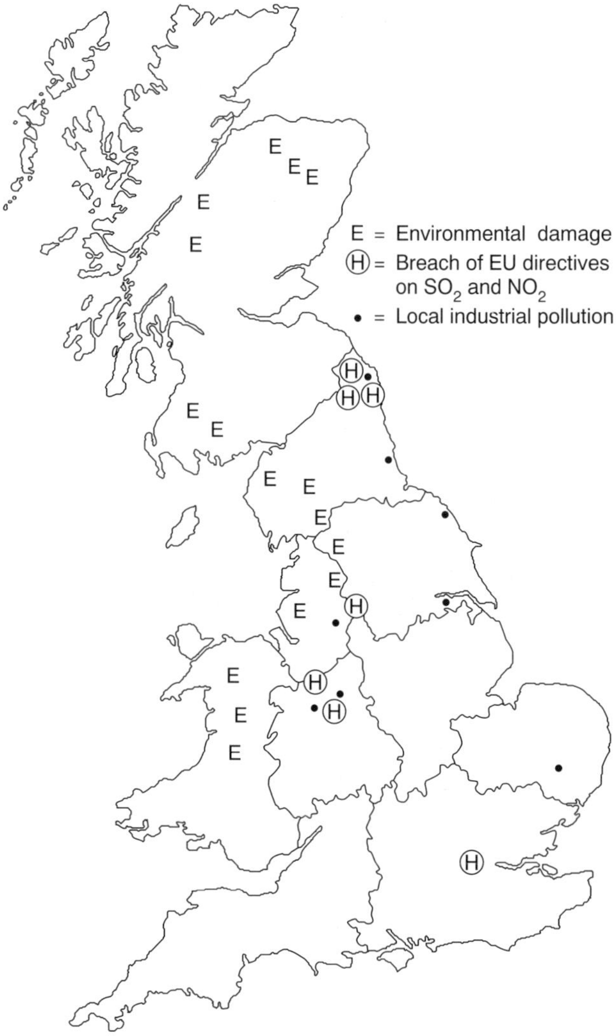

E = Environmental damage
Ⓗ = Breach of EU directives on SO$_2$ and NO$_2$
• = Local industrial pollution

Figure 24.12 Air Quality

AIR POLLUTION TOTAL EMISSIONS: UNITED KINGDOM 1971–1991

	Nitrogen Dioxide	Sulphur Dioxide
1971	2 260 000	6 060 000
1981	2 300 000	4 440 000
1991	2 750 000	3 570 000
(Tonnes)		

Figure 24.14

- Some pollution is localised, others can affect areas many miles away from the source
- Exhaust fumes have risen by 75% since 1980 and the level of traffic will increase between 65% and 106% by 2025 (Department of Transport)

Figure 24.15

AIR POLLUTION: SULPHUR DIOXIDE EMISSIONS BY REGION 1971–1991

	1971	1975	1991
North	94	55	28
Yorks/Humber	158	82	36
E Midlands	105	57	39
E Anglia	65	55	17
Gtr London	203	103	42
Rest South East	79	58	34
South West	75	48	19
W Midlands	117	79	39
North West	150	83	40
Wales	72	53	26
Scotland	64	50	33
(Micrograms per cubic metre)			

AIR POLLUTION BY SOURCE: UNITED KINGDOM 1992

	Sulphur Dioxide	Nitrogen Dioxide
Road Transport	2	51
Electricity Supply	69	25
Domestic	3	3
Other	26	21
(Percentages)		

Figure 24.13

AIR POLLUTION (SULPHUR DIOXIDE FROM FUEL COMBUSTION): UNITED KINGDOM 1951–1977

	1951	1971	1977
Industry	2 290 000	610 000	330 000
Power Stations	1 020 000	2 800 000	2 750 000
Domestic	870 000	440 000	270 000
Fuel, Coal, Petrol	550 000	2 000 000	1 640 000
(Tonnes)			

- Atmospheric conditions affect pollution – winter temperature inversions stagnate air, summer heat increases photochemical action

Figure 24.16

Asthma

- Medically, an unclassified disease, difficult to explain and with many possible causes
- An inflammation of the airways to, and in, the lungs causing breathing difficulties
- Pollutants are not believed to medically cause asthma, but they can make it much worse, or bring on an attack
- Certain individuals are more susceptible and many allergens can affect sufferers – smoking, dust mites, pollen and air pollutants
- Nitrogen dioxide and ozone are particularly implicated as they affect the lungs and respiration
- The pollen count peaks earlier in the day in rural areas compared to urban areas (and is more difficult to avoid because of this). In urban areas, the evening pollen peaks are greater than the morning peaks
- Other factors can affect sufferers, though the mechanisms are not well understood: colds, passive smoking, cold weather and thunderstorms (on 24 June 1994, 1,500 extra out-of-hours calls were made to doctors because of asthma alone in south-east England, an area suffering severe thunderstorms at the time)
- After heart disease and strokes, it is now the third major reason for hospital admissions in the UK (100,000 people were admitted with asthma in 1996)
- 7 million working days are lost in the UK annually through asthma
- 750,000 children miss some school because

Figure 24.17

- 'Environmental factors play a key role in triggering allergy' (British Thoracic Society, 1997)
- More than one in four adults will suffer allergies like asthma by the year 2019
- The 1952 London smog caused 4000 deaths and was largely due to sulphur dioxide and ozone pollution

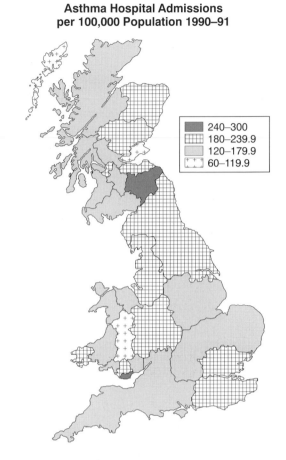

Figure 24.18 Asthma

AVERAGE DWELLING PRICE BY REGION 1992/1997		
	1992	**1997**
North	£48 300	£51 762
Yorks/Humber	£52 200	£53 171
E Midlands	£54 600	£57 387
E Anglia	£56 700	£63 180
Gtr London	£78 300	£97 043
Rest South East	£74 300	£88 443
South West	£61 500	£69 358
W Midlands	£57 800	£67 139
North West	£56 400	£55 340
Wales	£49 700	£54 202
Scotland	£49 200	£58 861

Figure 24.19

25   *Native Americans: Zuñi Pueblo, New Mexico*

One of the most difficult techniques to master is that which requires that you use 'empathy', the ability to mentally associate intimately with the views and feelings of other people. Frequently, the decisions you make affect others more than you, so you really should try to see their viewpoint. The exercise below casts you in two very different roles to test your empathic abilities. The information is real, but the precise scenario is fictitious.

People often preserve ancient traditions even though the situation they find themselves in has radically altered. The cinema image of the American Indian (more correctly referred to as the *Native American*) used to be that of a noble savage or a ferocious red devil, and tended to be drawn unsympathetically in a white, Anglocentric, degrading manner – what would a Native American think?

Compare the words of these American Presidents with the lyrics of the song.

'What is the right of the huntsman to the forest of 1000 miles over which he has accidentally ranged in quest of prey?'

(President John Quincy Adams, 1802)

Elu homa Yallanne!

Awehlwia kwai-i
Imuna Kwagia
Lonan-eshto 'wiyane

Liwamani
Iyuteapa
Awiyane
Hawilana litla

O my lovely mountain yallane
Clouds high up in the sky
See rainmakers seated
Hither come the rainclouds now
Behold, yonder
All will soon be blooming
Where the flowers spring
Tall will grow the corn plants

(*Ockaya* – a traditional Zuñi corn-grinding song to the harvest)

The hunter or savage state requires a greater extent of territory than is compatible with the just claims of civilised life ... and must yield to it'

(President James Monroe, 1817)

Decision-Making Exercise

The proposed development is for a new State Highway from point 'A' to point 'B'. Construction will cost $50 000 per mile and the road will affect a buffer zone one mile on either side of the road. The road can only be built in New Mexico territory.

1 In your first role, you are asked to assume the identity of a civil engineer from Boston, working for the New Mexico Highways Authority (NMHA). You are to find a route for a state highway from point A to point B according to one overriding criterion – cost. It must be the cheapest route possible, irrespective of all other factors except topography.

   • Draw your route on the map
   • Cost your route

   This is now the official route proposed by the NMHA.

2 In your second role, you are asked to assume the identity of a Zuñi tribal member, who went to the University of New Mexico at Albuquerque and studied to become an ethnogeographer. The Zuñi are extremely concerned at the proposals and have asked your help to devise an alternative route more akin to their needs, in terms of protection of their tribal heritage, developments to improve tourism receipts and other measures to improve their lot.

From the information provided:
   • derive and draw an alternative route
   • cost the new route
   • briefly explain the methods you used to find the route
   • write a full, detailed justification in two parts:
     – Part one to show the Zuñi how the project might help them
     – Part two to justify, in detail, the alternative route to the NMHA. Also, include other measures that the State could implement to help your people.

Social/Mining Facilities

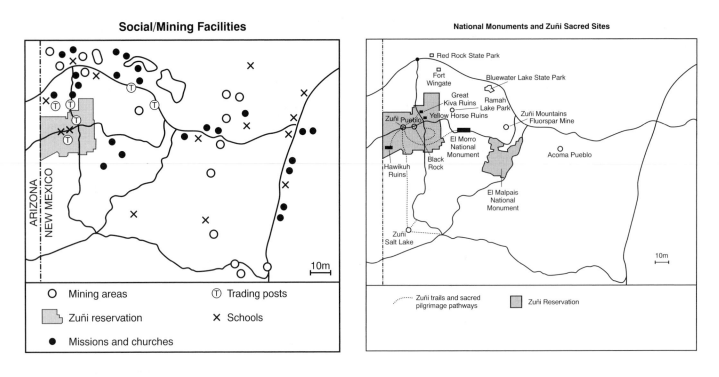

Figure 25.2

National Monuments and Zuñi Sacred Sites

Figure 25.3

Indian Reservations

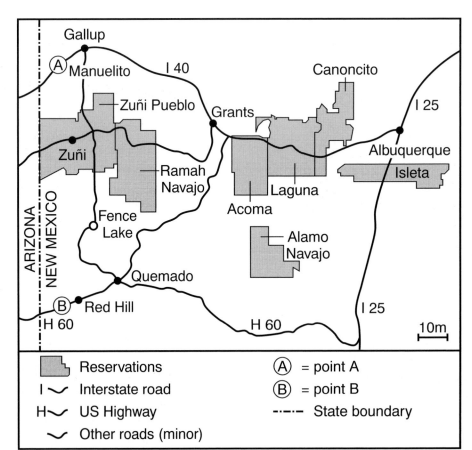

Figure 25.1

Physical Features

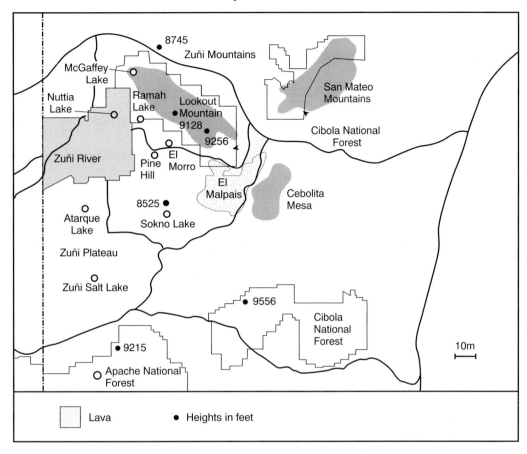

Figure 25.4

New Mexico Facts

- Population 1993: 1 616 000
- Area: 121 593 sq. miles
- State capital: Santa Fe
- Spanish, then Mexican and finally US territory (1848)
- Became a US State in 1912
- Land ownership:
  44.1% Private
  34.3% Federal
  12.1% State
   9.4% Native American

Figure 25.6

Month	Temperature °F		Precipitation Inches
	Max	Min	
Jan	47	23	0
Feb	53	27	0
Mar	59	32	0
Apr	70	41	0
May	80	51	1
Jun	89	60	1
July	92	65	1
Aug	90	63	1
Sep	83	57	1
Oct	72	45	1
Nov	57	32	0
Dec	47	25	1

CLIMATIC INDICATORS (AT ALBUQUERQUE)

Figure 25.5

**USA NATIVE AMERICAN POPULATION:
FIVE TOP STATES**

State	Pop. 1980	Rank 1980	Pop. 1890	Rank 1890
California	201 311	1	15 283	5
Oklahoma	169 464	2	74 997*	1
Arizona	152 857	3	16 740	4
New Mexico	104 777	4	28 799	2
North Carolina	64 635	5	3 116	18

*(As the Indian Territory)
In 1980, the USA had 270 Indian Reservations, housing about 50% of the 1 400 000 Native Americans in the country

Figure 25.7

Figure 25.9 'Sky City' (Acoma Pueblo) 1993

Some Relevant General Legislation/Policies/Movements

- 1887 General Allotment Act – divided Indian Reservations into 160 acre lots for Indian families, the remaining land was available for sale (assimilation policy)
- 1906 Antiquities Act – created 'National Monuments', areas of special archaeological, historical or scientific importance
- 1921 Snyder Act – Department of the Interior responsible for Indian social, educational and medical services
- 1922 All Pueblo Council established
- 1924 Citizens Act – Indians became citizens, but New Mexico withheld their right to vote
- 1934 Indian Reorganisation Act – repealed 1887 Act and allowed self-government in Reservations, Indian business companies and tribal landholding
- 1944 National Congress of American Indians established
- 1950s 'Termination Acts' – policy to remove Federal responsibility for some tribes
- 1960s 'Self-determination Acts' – policy for self-government on Reservations and wide struggle to preserve heritage and rights of Indians

- 1961 National Indian Youth Council established in Gallup
- 1968 American Indian Movement (AIM) established – pressure group to regain lands and rights. Beginnings of 'Red Power' protest movement
- 1969 Environmental Policy Act – protection for Indian resources
- 1973 AIM under armed siege at Wounded Knee, protesting at poverty and unemployment
- 1974 Indian Financing Act – policy for development of businesses (1982–87 Indian businesses increased in number by 64%, compared to 14% for all US businesses)
- 1974 Housing and Community Development Act – to build new Indian housing
- 1978 American Indian Freedom of Religion Act
- 1991 Native American Graves and Repatriation Act – allows tribes to claim back bones and artefacts from graves, or items of artistic, cultural or religious significance currently in museums
- 1991 New Mexico Indian Tourism Program established with $100 000 State aid to develop tourism businesses and activities

Figure 25.8

ZUÑI PUEBLO: US CENSUS OF POPULATION
(Ranks based on 20 largest American Indian Reservations – rank 1 highest)

- Estimated Population: Rank
    1680   2 500
    1970   4 736   7
    1980   5 988   7
    1990   5 857   7
- Percentage owner-occupied housing:
    1970   92.5%   1
    1980   68.6%   6
- Median Rooms per dwelling:
    1970   4.5   2
    1980   5.1   2
- Percentage dwellings with more than 1 person per room:
    1970   70.5%   2
    1980   42.2%   8
- Percentage dwelling units less than 10 years old:
    1970   28.8%   9
    1980   42.8%   9
- Value of owner occupied dwellings:
    1970 $13 327   5
    1980 $21 800   6
- Educational attainment of residents over 25 years of age:
    Graduate High School
    1970   18.5%   11
    1980   37.3%   14
    Graduate College
    1970   0.2%   14
    1980   2.1%   13
    Attend tribal school
    1970   5.2%   13
- Employment:
    In employment
    1970   30.2%   14
    1980   79.7%   1
    Unemployment rate
    1970   14.9%   8
    1980   23.2%   10
    In traditional occupations
    1980   26.6%   1 (next largest Hopi at 6.3%)
- Median family income:
    1969 $10 476   1
    1979 $10 354   6
- Families below poverty line:
    1969   56.7%   8
    1979   44.6%   10
- Percentage families on BIA assistance;
    1979   1.1%   16
- Immigration onto reservation:
    Always lived here   89.7%   3
    1979/80   2.2%   16
    1975/79   3.0%   13
    Before 1975   5.1%   14

Figure 25.10

Zuñi History

- *Anasazi*, the 'ancient ones' settled Arizona and New Mexico in prehistoric period, living in multi-room cliff and rock dwellings. Developed agriculture around 100AD. Ancestors of Zuñi and other Pueblo tribes. Drought and over-planting led to demise (dendrochronological records show a severe drought from 1276 to 1299).
- 1529 Estavan the Moor (the first black man in American historical records) killed by Zuñi for impersonating a god and 'assaulting Zuñi women' – after telling Spanish of fabled treasure in the area.
- 1539 Fra. Marcos de Niza saw Zuñi Pueblo, then at *Hawikuh*, in the distance in evening sunlight and reported to Spain that its 'house doors are studded with jewels, streets lined with shops of silversmiths, a beautiful city … bigger than the City of Mexico'.
- 1540 Spanish Governor Coronado, believing it to be one of the rich 'Seven Cities of Cibola', took the settlement, to find only an adobe mud and stone agricultural village ('a small round pueblo, all crumpled up').
- 1680 Zuñi took part in the Pueblo Revolt, temporarily (until 1692) ousting the Spaniards.
- 1877 Zuñi Reservation created on ancient lands – a Federal Reservation.
- 1970 Zuñi Reservation first Native American community to administer its own area.
- 1990 Zuñi Salt Lake Project to develop an open-cast strip coal mine near the ancient and revered site of ritual and saleable salt, with sacred pilgrimage trails. Tribes used endangered species, historical preservation and heritage legislation against the proposal, but failed to stop its development.

Figure 25.11

Zuñi Philosophy

- When the Creator made the world, the profound complexity of the universe was so far beyond human comprehension that the Creator gave each group a tiny glimpse of the whole truth.
- A sense of continuity with the land. Zuñis say that Anglos and Mexicans have no respect for the land and abuse it rather than work with it.
- Land supports life, it is beautiful because of this and must be preserved.
- Land is a living being, a spiritual relative to all Zuñi.
- Sense of permanence, of an infinite past that implies an infinite future.
- That which you strive for in this world is *hózhó* (beauty, balance, harmony). Your home and environment are your church, your place of prayers.
- A spiritual view of the world that places humans within the web of life rather than above it.

Figure 25.13 Zuñi Pueblo in 1880's with Yallane, the Corn Mountain

- Special care is given to maintaining a healthy balance between the inhabitants of the Pueblo and the Earth.
- Zuñi mythology has six cardinal directions:
  North – land of the Mountain Lion
  South – land of the Badger
  East – land of the Wolf
  West – land of the Bear
  Sky – land of the Eagle
  Inner earth – land of the Mole

Figure 25.12

Zuñi Philosophy Continued

Zuñi Pueblo is located at the 'Middle Place' in this scheme of directions, the heartbeat of the world

- The concept of a map is different. To the Zuñi, a depiction of stylized lines, symbols, dots and geometric patterns in what looks to us like an impressionist painting, is a map with all the essential spatial features for finding your way.
- *Kivas* are the round ceremonial subterranean chambers in the centre of the Pueblo, sacred places not open to the public.
- *Kachinas* are the spiritual beings who bring harmony between humans and the world. They are sold as dolls and appear in ritual ceremonies as dancers.
- *Yallane* – a mountain, and *lonan-eshto* – rainclouds, are central to ceremonies and life in a region of sparse precipitation and uncertain water supplies.

- *Kwagia* – rainmakers, are still the principal Zuñi individuals, and their spiritual counterparts inhabit the sky, with clouds to hide their sacred faces from humans.
- Pueblo groups are non-individualistic and make group decisions in a highly organized community.
- In 1946, the rite of *Hanasema Isu Waha*, or purification, was performed at Zuñi Pueblo on GIs returning after the Second World War, or 'War of the Whites'.
- The *Shalako* Festival takes place every December and is open to the public, at which the Great Bird *Kachinas* bless new or rebuilt houses, to ensure the future prosperity at the Winter Solstice.
- The Zuñi have a complicated mix of Catholic religion and tribal ceremony and traditions.
- Zuñi society is matrilineal.

Miscellaneous Information

- *Pueblo* – Spanish for village or town, a highly organised community
- *Adobe* – bricks mad of mud and sun-dried (most of Zuñi Pueblo is brick covered in plaster, but looks the same warm red colour)
- Zuñi make and trade in/sell to tourists:
     Silver and turquoise jewellery (the Zuñi colour of heaven)
     Traditional pottery
     Kachina dolls and animal fetishes
     Agricultural produce – chillies, squash
     Spirit masks
- Many Zuñi work in neighbouring towns
- Trading Posts were originally set up as exchange/barter/sale points between Indian tribes and the Anglos, or whites
- 'Zuñi' is pronounced 'Zoo-nye'
- *To'yallane* – the Corn, Lookout or Thunder mountain to the east is sacred to Zuñi, a place of pilgrimage

Figure 25.15 Zuñi pueblo dwelling c. 1900

- Permission is needed to enter *Hawikuh*, ancient Zuñi Pueblo site, and *Great Kiva Ruins*, an unexcavated and sacred site of pueblo settlement
- Only Federal and tribal (not State) laws apply in Indian Reservations

Figure 25.14

**Miscellaneous
Information
Continued**

Figure 25.16 Indian
Reservation,
New Mexico 1993

• The present
Zuñi
Pueblo is at
7000 feet
above sea
level and
was first
occupied in
1699

• Gallup is the main off-reservation urban Indian settlement in the USA. It was established as a railroad town to exploit the large coal reserves in the area
• *El Morro National Monument* is a Zuñi sandstone mountain and includes the 'Inscription rock' on which prehistoric Indians left petroglyphs and Juan de Onate started the fashion of travellers leaving inscriptions in 1605. There is an ancient Zuñi pueblo ruin at the top
• *Black Rock* sacred to Zuñi
• There are many sacred pilgrimage trails in the area, many ill-defined

• *El Malpais National Monument and National Conservation Area* is an area of extensive lava flows – the words mean 'badlands'
• Interstate 40 is along the line of the famous Trans-American *Route 66*

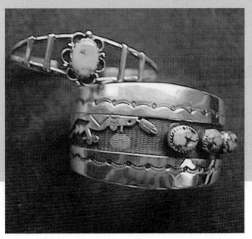

Figure 25.17 Silver
and turquoise
jewellery with
Kachina motif

Figure 25.14 continued

26 *Celebrating the Millennium through History*

It is important that we understand the uses and limitations of both our methods and our source materials when making decisions. Quite often, sources may be only partial, they may be of questionable accuracy, or even of little real value to our analyses or decision-making. They may use techniques that we know about and can therefore 'question'. We really do need to evaluate our materials before using them to make our decisions.

This exercise, though fictional, uses unaltered historical sources. The aerial photograph referred to in the letter is Figure 23.2 on page 76.

Phoenix and Wilson,
Public Relations
122, Elmwood Road
London
EE12 5HQ
REF: DART355

Dear ....,

We have been retained by the town of Dartford in Kent to organize one aspect of their Millennium celebrations for the year 2000. You have been recommended to us as an expert in the use of historical geographical sources and we would like your help on a particular project which may interest you. Remuneration will be at our usual rates.

The project is provisionally entitled 'Celebrating the Millennium through History' and we intend to use it to show visitors in 2000 what the town was like in history, specifically in 1850.

Fortunately, we have found a rich source of data in a wooden chest of material collected by a local antiquarian bookseller, one Ezekiel Solomon. We know that Ezekiel was born in 1800 and died in 1900, so the year 2000 fits the sequence nicely! We also know that he had the idea of presenting displays at appropriate places in Dartford to show visitors what the town was like around 1850 (this was to celebrate the Great Exhibition in the following year) and that was why he collected the information we have now unearthed. He was never able to complete his project, but we hope to do it for him!

Your task is to advise us, using the materials enclosed, and to produce:

1 An annotated summary map of Dartford around 1850, showing the main geographical characteristics of the town and its people, that we could publish for sale to visitors in 2000.
2 A brief four-page written explanation of the characteristics of the town around 1850, to go with the map.
3 A second map identifying at least two sites in the present town where we could erect information displays on that specific locality as it was around 1850, with a brief summary of what we could provide as illustrative information. You will need to tell us why we should use those particular sites.
4 As we are using old sources, you will need to provide short evaluations of each of Ezekiel's sources for us and, particularly where we have only been able to find extracts from sources, advise us as to what use we could make of them if we wanted more detailed analysis and could discover the full resource.

Ezekiel's material is attached:

* Figure 26.1 A portion of the Enumerator's Returns of the Census of 1851.
* Figure 26.2 Samual Bagshaw's *History, Gazetteer and Directory of Dartford*, 1847. This was produced for popular sale and Ezekiel comments that 'Bagshaw was a truthful and competent purveyor of information'.
* Figure 26.3 A portion of William Ranger's Sanitary Report to the General Board of Health on Dartford, 1849. Ezekiel says: 'The townsfolk were mightily upset to have such depredations revealed in public'.
* Figure 26.4 A portion of the Tithe Map of Dartford, 1840. These showed land liable to pay tithes (tenths of produce) to the church and so are accurate on boundaries as they showed who was to pay what, and when the tithes were changed to money rents.
* Figure 26.5 A print of the High Street, Dartford, 1860
* Figure 26.6 Ordnance Survey First edition map of Dartford, 1866
* Figure 26.7 A Perry's *Directory of Dartford*, 1871

To help you, we also attach a series of recent (1997) photographs of the town, an Ordnance Survey map portion from 1974 (Figure 26.8) and an aerial photograph taken in 1953. We look forward to receiving your report.

Yours sincerely,

George Wilmslow

Parish or Township of *Dartford*	Ecclesiastical District of	City or Borough of	Town of	Village of				
Name of Street, Place, or Road, and Name or No. of House	Name and Surname of each Person who abode in the house, on the Night of the 30th March, 1851	Relation to Head of Family	Condition	Age of Males	Age of Females	Rank, Profession, or Occupation	Where Born	Whether Blind, or Deaf-and-Dumb
27 *High Street* *Bull & George*	*William A Meyers*	*Head*	*Mar*	39		*Licensed Victualler*	*Middlesex Bloomsbury*	
	Caroline Do	*Wife*	*Mar*		39		*Do Mile End*	
	William T Do	*Son*		10		*Scholar*	*Do Clerkenwell*	
	Isabella M Do	*Daur*			7	*Do*	*Do Do*	
	Catherine Do	*Daur*			5	*Do*	*Do Mile End*	
	Henry Do	*Son*		3			*Do Do*	
	Lea Do	*Son*		11mo			*Kent Dartford*	
	Ann Laws	*Serv*	*U*		23	*General Serv*	*Middlesex Mile End*	
	Susan Hills	*Serv*	*U*		15	*Nurse Maid*	*Kent Dartford*	
	William Wickham	*Serv*		17		*Pot Boy*	*Do Do*	
28 *Bull & George*	*Sarah Coney*	*Head*	*W*		40	*Licensed Victualler*	*Do Do*	
Yup	*Sarah E Do*	*Daur*			14	*Scholar*	*Do Do*	
29 *High Street*	*Thomas Garrett*	*Head*	*Mar*	53		*Lodging House Keeper*	*Kent Strood*	
	Maria Do	*Wife*	*Mar*		55		*Do Wrotham*	
	Thomas Do	*Son*	*U*	22		*Cordwanier*	*Do Strood*	
	George Do	*Son*	*U*	14		*Scholar*	*Do Do*	
	Elizabeth Hamilton	*Lodger*	*Mar*		32	*Traveller Pauper*	*Middlesex St Giles*	
	Richard Cherry	*Do*	*Mar*	38		*Do Do*	*Kent Meopham*	
	Eliza S Wilson	*Do*	*U*		59	*Do Do*	*Do Wrotham*	
	Catherine Bright	*Do*	*Mar*		37	*Do Do*	*Do Welling*	
3 B				Total of Persons	6 11			

Figure 26.1 A portion of the Enumerator's Returns of the Census 1851

Figure 26.2 Samuel Bagshaw's *History, Gazetteer and Directory of Dartford*, 1871

CLARK'S ALLEY.—The only access to this place, there being no thoroughfare, is by a covered passage, 6 feet 6 inches high by 3 feet 6 inches wide; a privy for all the houses being under one of the houses, and close to the front door. The general character of this place is such that human beings ought not to be allowed to occupy it. The major part of the smaller class dwellings in this place have been erected regardless of common decency, not to say cleanliness; and as one poor but well-conducted woman remarked, "How can we be clean in these places? they are not fit for human beings to live in."

OVERCROWDING.—In the course of my inspection several instances of overcrowded dwellings were met with. The following may be taken as samples:—

In Webb's Alley, a man, wife, and seven children, the eldest 19 years of age, and the youngest 16 months, occupy one small room, 10 feet by about 10 feet, for sleeping. At Short Hill I found in one room a man, wife, and sister, 16 years of age, and several children. To mention but one other instance of a similar character, a widow with five children live together in one room, the eldest, a son, 20, and the youngest, a girl, 12 years of age.

PRESENT DRAINAGE.—The rivers Darent and Cranford form the arterial drainage of the defile in which the town is seated. But from various obstructions to their natural course, and their having been converted into receptacles for filth, etc., from the town, a considerable amount of deposit or silting up has been caused, and to such an extent that even the works of the new creek made to facilitate the navigation has not obviated the evil, although there is a fall of about 25 feet below the top of the Tumbling Bay at Phoenix Mills; and the evil is further increased by an occasional flooding of the marshes.

It has already been shown that on the north side of the town stagnant water is found to such an extent that the most malignant forms of fever are liable to supervene; whilst the marshes in a north-easterly direction extending from the town to the bank of the Thames (and included in the parish and drainage area), contain no less than 30 acres of surface in ditches, all more or less filled with decayed but stagnant vegetable matter, etc.

Mr. Culhane, surgeon, in alluding to the permanent nuisances, says: "The noxious miasmatic character of the stagnant pools and ditches I have been called upon to see; particularly the one separating properties on the north side of the town, and running parallel to Spital Street; the mephitic effluvia issuing from this one source alone (out of the many) is of the kind destructive to human life."

The works of the railway have added to this class of evils by impeding the natural drainage in numerous gardens and yards, particularly in the east side of every street, where the cesspools, entering the toe of the chalk, intercept the water in its passage. There are other nuisances of the same character. The lower end of Water-side (forming the outfall of a stream running down or rather occupying the entire width of roadway to a considerable depth, with stepping-blocks to enable the inhabitants to cross from one side to the other), having been, as stated by Mr. Cresy, considerably raised in its bed, probably by the deposits during the time the waters are pent back by the tidal action of the waters in the creek, constitutes a permanent nuisance, in its effect prejudicial to the health of those residing on its banks; in addition to this, a space on the opposite side of the creek has been converted into a landing place for manure, discharged from barges, plying between this town and the metropolis.

The average annual mortality for the parish during six years, i.e., from 1838 to 1844, amounts to 23 in 1,000; and for the following statistical results I am indebted to Mr. E. Cresy, junior, from whom I have derived other highly important information.

The deaths from all causes between February 1847 and 1848, out of a population of about 5,600, amounted to 327; and the principal diseases statistically classified, according to their fatality, is as follows:—

Phthisis	31
Typhus	24
Bronchitis	22
Pneumonia	22
Fever	19
Old Age	19
Small-pox	14
Diarrhœa	14
Apoplexy	13
Atrophy	11
Enteritis	10

Taking the months in the order of unhealthiness, we have for:—

November	37
December and August equal, each 35	70
October	34
March	32
June	27
February	26
April	22
January and September equal, each 21	42
July	16
May	15

Now, although the months appear to alternate in an irregular manner, the anomaly vanishes if we group them into quarters thus:—

First quarter	73
Second quarter	64
Third quarter	72
Fourth quarter	108

By this it appears the last quarter is nearly double that of the second.

SEATS OF DISEASE.—Mr. Tippetts, surgeon to the Union, observes, that most of the cases of fever of a malignant character falling under his care have occurred in Water Lane and its vicinity, and mentions Webb's Court especially, as being inhabited by persons of the lowest and dirtiest grade, mostly with large families, and rendered the seat of fever of a most malignant, contagious and destructive quality. He further adds: "I have invariably found, that immediately fresh people take possession of these wretched tenements, they are attacked with fever"; in fact, he does not remember ever having been without a case (of fever) in this neighbourhood. The approach to this court is by a covered passage, 6 feet high by 4 feet wide, having at the opposite end piggeries, a dung-heap, and other accumulations of filth upon the surface.

KENT'S YARD contains a slaughter-house and five dwellings, without any outlets at back. In one I found the occupants labouring under severe fever. Across this yard there are two privies, the soil from drainage and slaughter-house being swilled into the river. To mention one other locality:

Figure 26.3 A portion of William Ranger's *Sanitary Report tto he General Board of Health in Dartford*, 1849

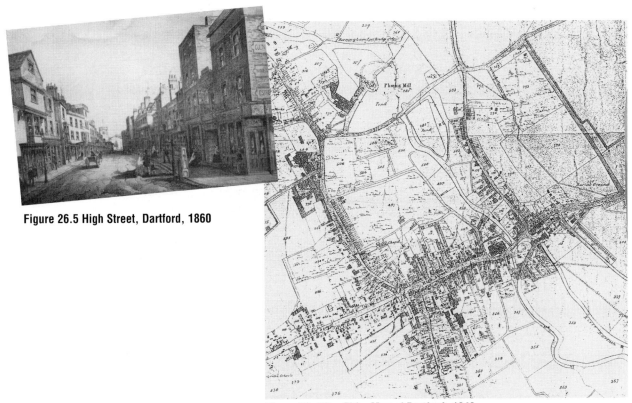

Figure 26.5 High Street, Dartford, 1860

Figure 26.4 The Tithe Map of Dartford, 1840

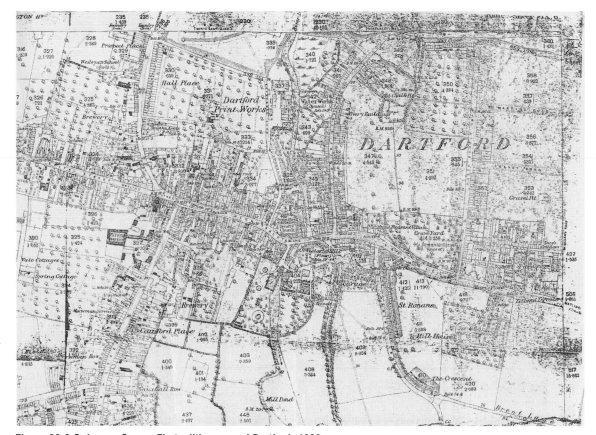

Figure 26.6 Ordnance Survey First edition map of Dartford, 1866

DARTFORD
COMMERCIAL DIRECTORY,
FOR 1871.

Magistrates.

Arbuthnot, W. U., Esq., Bridgen Place
Bradford, R., Esq., Franks
Bevan, Thomas, Stone Park
Currie, Sir F., Bart., Crayford
Chapman, J., Esq., Paul's Cray
Dashwood, Maitland, Esq., Bexley
Dyke, Sir P. H., Bart., Lullingstone
Dyke, W. H., Esq., M.P., Lullingstone
Fleet, T. H., Esq., Suttom-lace
Lewin, P. M., Esq., Half-way-street
Umfreville, S. C., Esq., Ingress Abbey
Wheatley, Colonel William, Erith
White, R. O., Esq., Lewisham
Petty Sessions held at the Court House,
Dartford, every alternate Saturday
Clerk to Magistrates, J. Hayward

Post Office.

Post and Money Order Office, Post Office
Savings Bank, Government Annuity, Insurance, and Telegraph Office,—George Hodges, Postmaster,
High-street.
Letters dispatched to London, 9.15, a.m.
1.0, p.m., 3.15, p.m., 8.15, p.m.
10.0, p.m.: Gravesend and Maidstone, 4.15, p.m.: Gravesend, Rochester, Maidstone, Chatham, Sittingbourne, and Sheerness, 9.30, p.m.
Letters arrive from London and all parts,
10.30, p.m., 9.30, a.m., and 4.45, p.m.: delivered at Dartford, 7.0,
a.m., 10.0, a.m., and 6.15, p.m.
Post Box, East Hill, Cleared at 9 a.m.,
12.40 and 7.50 p.m.
Post Box, West Hill, cleared at 6.30,
a.m., 12.30, p.m., and 5.40, p.m.:
Sundays at 6.30, a.m., only.
Money orders issued and paid 9.0, a.m.
till 6.0, p.m.; on Saturdays till 8.0,
p.m.

Churches and Chapels.

Holy Trinity Church) Rev. H. B. Bowl-
Christ Church) by, M.A., vicar, Revds. G. C. Fisher
and C. A. James, curates.
Wesleyan, Minister. Rev. W. Seed
Independent, Rev. J. H. Bowhay
High Field Road, Baptist, Rev. A. Sturge
Zion, no resident
Roman Catholic, Father Maurice

Public Institutions.

Board of Health,—J Hayward, Clerk;
J. Smith, Treasurer
County Court,—Spital-street, J. Lonsdale,
Judge ; John Hayward, Registrar;
Edward Augustus Hilder, Bailiff;
Thomas Hodsoll Pearce, Sub-bailiff
Excise Officer, J. P. Boutle
Corn & Cattle Market,—Corn on Saturday, and Cattle first Tuesday in
every month
Clerk to Commissioners of Sewers, from
Charlton to Gravesend, J. Hayward;
Treasurer, J. Smith
Clerk to Board of Guardians, John Hayward; Treasurer, J Smith
Clerk to Dartford and Crayford Navigation Commissioners, J. Hayward
Clerk to the Burial Board, C. R. Gibson
Churchwardens, J. Hayward, E. A. Quait
Collector of Creek Dues, J. G. Cann
Gas Works,—Waterside. Luke Green,
Manager. Office, Spital Street,
G. Kingston, Secretary, J. G. Cann,
Collector
Inspector of Nuisances,—George Bolt,
Dartford Road, assistant, C. Sharp
Inspector of Weights and Measures, J.
Webb, Overy Street
London and County Bank,—J. Smith,
Manager
Overseers,—R. Webb and C. Croshaw.
Assistant Overseer and Collector,—
J. Webb, Overy Street
Police Station,—High Field Road,
Christopher Brandon, Superintendent
Railway Station,—Peter Harvey, Station Master
Registrar of Marriages, George W. C.
Bonner, Dartford Road
Stamp Office,—High Street, A. Perry,
Distributor
Working Men's Institute,—High Street,
W. Cogger, Hon. Sec.
Union House,—(for 21 parishes) West
Hill, Rev. T. E. Gardner, Chaplain ;
R. H. Hunter, surgeon; Thomas
Wills, master; Mrs. Mary Jane
Wills, matron; Mrs. Tolhurst,
school assistant; E. Smith, relieving officer

Public Schools.

Grammar, Rev. R. Langbridge, master
British School, Highfield Road, Miss
Clarke, mistress
Infant, Hythe Street, Miss Susannah
Pitson, mistress
National, Spital Street, James Watts,
master; Miss Armes, mistress
Wesleyan (Girls), Hall Place, Miss
Raddenbury, mistress
Wesleyan (Boys), Spital street, J. Gayton, master
Roman Catholic, Hythe Street, Mrs.
O'Murphy, mistress

Insurance Agents.

British Empire and Mutual Life—
A. H. Davis, 4, Omega Cottages,
Dartford Road
Commercial Union,—F. Pelton, High-st
General,—A. J. Dunkin, High-street
Kent Fire and Life,—J. Sharp, High-st.
Liverpool, London, and Globe,—G. W.
Bonner, Dartford Road, and James
Seager, Darenth
Manchester Fire,—J. Lodge, Overy-st.
Midland Counties.—William Thomas
Stidolph, High-street
Mutual Life,—Thomas Kerr, High-st.
Norwich Union,—Wm. Thomas Bray,
Bull Hotel, High-st.
Phoenix Fire,—Arthur Perry, High-st.
and Henry Scott, Miskin Road
Reliance Life,—W. T. Bray, High-st.
Royal Fire & Life,—Edward Mackney,
2, Ebenezer Place, Lowfield-st.
Royal Exchange,—R. R. Hards, Royal
Victoria Mills
Standard Life,—A. E. Horrell, High-st.
and John; Webb, Overy-st.
Sun Fire,—Fedk. W. Boyce, East Hill
Westminster Fire & Life,—J. C. Martin,
Spital-st.
Whittington Life,—W. Sandy, East
Hill

FIRE ENGINE STATIONS.

Royal Exchange—Royal Mill, near the
Bridge ; Thomas Tile, conductor,
Bullace lane
Kent—Mr. Sharp's, Waterside, opposite
Catholic Chapel; T. Buckland, conductor, Lowfield Street
Norwich Union—Corner of Mr. Hall's
Factory, Waterside; Thomas Waller, conductor, corner of Orchard
Street, Waterside

Fire Escape kept at Messrs. Haywards'
yard, Spital Street ; E. Upton,
captain, High Street

Carriers.

Eynsford,—Francis Booker ; from One
Bell Inn, 12, noon, daily
London,—Percival Smale, from Lowfield
street, 8, a.m. daily ; Thomas Oliver
Walkling from West Hill, at 8.30,
a.m. daily
Water Conveyance to London, Waller's
Barges to and from. daily, from the
Wharf, Waterside.
Farningham,—Omnibus daily to and
from Dartford Railway Station,
three times per day.

Professions.

Solicitors,—Gibson, C. R., Lowfield St. ;
Haywards, Keele, & Swann, Spital
Street ; Russell, Son, and Scott,
Spital Street
Surgeons,—Croucher. H., Spital Street ;
Hoare, W.P., Lowfield St.; Hunter, R.
H., Bridge House; Martin, J.C., Spital
Street ; Moore, E., Spital Street

Trades.

Ackworth, Bros., candle makers, Orchard-st.
Agate, T., marine store dealer, Lowfield-st.
Alden, William, grocer, Gas-lane
Aldous, Miss, grocer, Hall-place
Allen, A. J. Dunkin, High-street
Allen, James, farmer, Stone-hill
Allen, Mary Ann, Mrs., grocer, Lowfield-st.
Applegath, L., printer, Orchard-street
Apted, William, Woodman Tavern, East-hill
Archer, William, greengrocer, Spital-street
Ashdown, M., bird stuffer, Lowfield-st., see
advertisement
Banks, F., baker, High-street
Barton, John, butcher, High-street
Bosworth, H. G., milliner, Lowfield-street
Batt, W., town crier & bill poster, Lowfield-st,
daylis, W. T., Rose and Crown, West-hill
Benson, Richard, baker, Hythe-street
Berrecloth, the Salutation, Heath-lane
Birmingham, Owen, shopkeeper, Hythe-st.
Black, G., New Inn, High-street
Blackman, W., New Town Tavern
Blower, W., basket maker, High-st., see advt.
Booker, Ship, Dartford-road
Borner, Thomas Edmund, dyer, Spital-street
Bolt, G., plasterer, Dartford-road
Bray, W. T., Bull Hotel, High-street
Buck, Edward, draper, High-street, see advt.
Buckland, T., sen., wheelwright, Lowfield-st.
Buckland, T., jun., shoemaker, Lowfield-st.
Bullock, Mrs., grocer, New-town
Bush, J., eating-house, High-street
Butlin, T. S., baker, Lowfield-street
Burns, cooper, East-hill
Bennett, G. W., greengrocer, Lowfield-street
Britton, G., shoemaker, Hythe-street

Figure 26.7 A Perry's *Directory of Dartford*, 1871

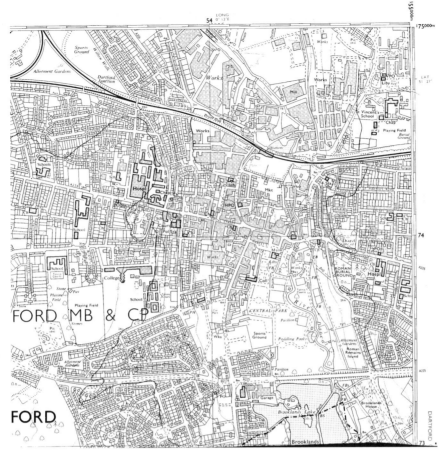

Figure 26.8 Ordnance Survey map of Dartford, 1974

Figure 26.10 Library and Park, 1998

Figure 26.9 High Street, 1998

Figure 26.11 The Wat Tyler, Bullace Lane, 1998

Figure 26.12 Royal Victoria and Bull Coaching Inn,
High Street, 1998

27 The 'Environmental' Issue

The question of environmental problems and what we should or should not do about them is an emotive issue. If such emotions (either way) are combined with quite detailed knowledge of the subject we might have difficulty arriving at an unbiased decision. This is not to imply that you should never include your strong views, and your knowledge of the subject may be invaluable – but

you do need to be aware of how they might affect your decision-making.

In the following scenario, you are asked to assume the identity of Dr Jones, an environmental geographer with a reputation for objective analysis, a wide knowledge of environmental problems, and media awareness.

Geoenv Publications
1023, Roswell Park Drive
Phoenix
Arizona 23457-78465
U.S.A.

Dear Dr Jones,

We are publishers of popular journals in the US in the fields of Geography, Environment and UFO studies. We are intending to enter the British journals market with a new product aimed at those members of the public concerned about, and interested in, environmental issues.

We had our market research department collect some material on Britain to help us to decide on the publication, but we do not know enough about your local circumstances to be able to make much sense of what we have gathered. This is where you come in – for the usual remuneration we would much appreciate your analysis of what our data shows and your considered opinions about our project.

Our material is attached, but we would expect you to use whatever other information you know, or can easily research from libraries or bookshops, to help us decide. We need to know:

1 What has been happening over the last 20 years to the 'environmental movement' in Britain:
    Has it been growing/declining and is it still growing/declining at the same rate?
    Is it what we call 'general public interest' or more 'activist interest' that has been growing/declining?

2 Are people in Britain affected most by local/national issues and problems or by global ones?

3 What attitudes do the people of Britain have on the environment – do they worry about it? Has this changed over time?

4 Are the British people taking personal environmental action themselves? Has this changed over time?

5 What main issues do existing magazines or journals in Britain appear to cover?

6 Is there any link at times between interest in the environment, expressed via journal publications, questionnaire surveys and membership of organizations and: particular 'general events' (like the Earth Summit) or particular environmental incidents or disasters?

7 On the basis of your analysis, we need to know if the proposed journal can sell.
    Is there enough environmental interest in Britain for our new journal?
    Should it appeal to the general public or to more 'active' environmentalists (or both)?
    What geographical scale should it cover – local, national, international or global?
    What should it cover – general problems, disasters, green solutions, organic gardening, practical environmentalism for families or what?
    Can you think of a suitable title for the journal?

Please let us have your report, with charts if possible, as soon as possible and we look forward to your contribution to our decision-making process.

Yours Sincerely,

Clara J Syston

Selected Environmental Events and Incidents 1967–1994

1967 *Torrey Canyon* tanker oil pollution off Land's End – 119 000 barrels crude oil pour into the sea.

1970 Earth Day – protests on university campuses for the environment.

1972 Plutonium works in New York closed permanently after fire.

1975 Browns Ferry, USA, nuclear incident, $100 000 damage.

1976 2 000 000 litres of radioactive water escape at Windscale, Cumberland.

1977 Ekofisk oilfield spillage, North Sea 31 040 000 litres.

1978 *Amoco Cadiz* oil pollution off France 223 000 barrels.
      Windscale Report – reprocessing nuclear waste allowed.
      Soviet nuclear-powered satellite crashes in Canada.

1979 Three Mile Island, Harrisburg, USA, nuclear reactor incident.

1980 UN call for ban on CFCs.
      Greenham Common protests at US nuclear weapons based in UK.

1981 Wildlife and Countryside Act.
      Iodine 101 contaminates milk around Windscale.

1982 Falklands War.

1984 Bhopal poison gas disaster, India.
      Sizewell B reactor approved after long inquiry (1982–84).
      Band Aid record released to raise funds for Ethiopian famine.

1985 Food and Environment Protection Act.
      Vienna Convention to protect ozone layer.
      Rainbow Warrior, Greenpeace ship sunk in Auckland.
      Ozone layer hole discovered in Antarctica.
      Green Party founded.
      Live Aid concert for famine relief.

1986 Chernobyl Nuclear power station disaster, Ukraine, USSR.
      Widespread radiation overEurope.
      BSE epidemic identified in Britain.

1987 European year of the Environment.
      Brundtland Report.
      Herald of Free Enterprise ferry disaster, Zeebrugge

1988 Camelford water poisoning incident.
      Piper Alpha oil exploration platform disaster, Scotland
      Salmonella in eggs scare.

1989 *Exxon Valdez* oil pollution, Alaska – 260 000 barrels discharged.
      Water Act.

1990 Town and Country Planning Act.
      Environment Protection Act.

1991 Food Safety Act.
      Gulf War, oil blowouts and pollution up to 585 000 000 litres.

1992 Earth Summit (UN Conference on Environment and Development), Rio de Janeiro, Brazil. Agenda 21 and sustainability.

1993 *The Countryside Survey* published, showing loss of hedges and wild flowers in Britain.
      Oil pollution from the oil tanker *Braer* off the Shetland Islands 85 000 tonnes.
      Tomsk, Siberia, uranium reprocessing plant explosion, radioactive pollution.

1994 Chemical leak pollutes water supply to 250 000 people in Shropshire/Worcestershire/ Gloucestershire.
      12 000 fish killed by sewage overflow on River Nene, Cambridgeshire.
      100 000 fish killed by slurry spillage on River Camel, Cornwall.

ENVIRONMENTAL GROUP ACTIVITIES: METHODS

(Parl = Parliamentary/constitutional work
Petit = Petitions
Direct = Direct action)

Group	Parl	Petit	Direct
ARK	√		√
BUAV			
Civic Trust	√	√	
Greenpeace	√		
Open Spaces Society	√	√	√
Soil Association	√		
Woodland Trust	√	√	
National Trust	√		
Friends of the Earth	√		
RSPB	√	√	√
Ramblers Association	√	√	
Green Alliance	√	√	
Transport 2000	√		
Urban Wildlife Trust	√		
Whale and Dolphin Conserv Soc	√	√	√
BTCV	√		√
CPRE	√	√	
RSNC	√	√	

Figure 27.1

Figure 27.2

Figure 27.3

SELECTED ENVIRONMENTAL ORGANISATIONS – APPROXIMATE MEMBERSHIP 1971–1993
(Note: data incomplete – not all responded and some have existed only recently)
(Figures in thousands)

Organisation	1971	1981	1987	1990	1991	1993
National Trust	278	950	1 545	1 750	2 152	2 189
Greenpeace		30	120	385	409	410
RSPB	98	321	561	844	852	850
Royal Soc Nature Cons	64	143	184	250	250	248
ARK				15	13	13
National Trust Scotland	37	110	160	218	234	235
Soil Association	4	4	5	6	6	
Civic Trust	214		240	293	222	222
Conservation Trust			3	2	9	12
World Wildlife Fund (WWF)	12	51	124	247	227	207
Woodland Trust	10	20	58	66	150	150
Friends of the Earth	1	12	55	120	111	120
Open Spaces Society			2.5	2.5	2.5	2.5
Ramblers Association	22	37	57	81	87	94
Watch Trust Env Educ		13	31	33	31	
Co Prot Rural England	21	27	32	44	45	45
Marine Conservation Soc		0.5	4	5.5		
Brit Trust Cons Volunteers	1	2			9	12
Young Peoples' Trust Env + Nature Conservation		0.8	133	280		

Figure 27.4

ENVIRONMENTAL ATTITUDES IN BRITAIN IV: HOW MUCH WILL ENVIRONMENTAL PROBLEMS AFFECT US?
(Percentage respondents)

Question	A Lot	Quite a lot
Are they affecting your health now?	17	37
Did they affect you 10 years ago?	7	20
Will they affect your children/ grandchildren?	47	35

Figure 27.7

ENVIRONMENTAL ATTITUDES IN BRITAIN II: INDIVIDUAL ACTIONS TAKEN
(Percentage of respondents already taking environmental action)

Action	1989	1993
Buy ozone-friendly products	63	65
Buy recycled paper	24	54
Use bottle banks	40	52
Collect newspapers for recycling	38	46
Buy unleaded petrol	23	38
Reduce use of cars	27	27
Buy biodegradeable products	8	43
Buy organic produce	6	46

(Based on Social Trends, HMSO)

Figure 27.5

ENVIRONMENTAL ATTITUDES IN BRITAIN III: CAUSES OF BRITAIN'S ENVIRONMENTAL PROBLEMS
(Percentage of respondents)

Cause	Percentage think a major element
Overpopulation	25
Government inaction	37
Wasteful People	60
Lack of knowledge of how to help	39
Uncaring industry	65
Technology creating pollution	53

Figure 27.6

ENVIRONMENTAL ATTITUDES IN BRITAIN I: ENVIRONMENTAL CONCERNS
(Percentage of respondents expressing strong concern on particular issues)

Concern	1988*	1989	1991*	1993
Chemical pollution waterways	85	64	84	63
Disposal of toxic waste			90	63
Disposal of radioactive waste	80	58	80	60
Ozone layer		56	81	41
Destruction rainforests	74	44	76	45
Acid rain	65	40	77	31
Global warming	70	44	71	35
Sewage on beaches	79	65	83	56
Oil on beaches	63	53	82	52
Loss of species in Britain				43
Loss of species in world	82		82	38
Air pollution from traffic	59	33	77	40
Air pollution from factories	61	34	71	35
Drinking water quality	64	41	70	38
Use of pesticides	70	46	81	36
Loss of greenbelt land	65	27	67	35
Loss of trees and hedges		34	70	36
Traffic congestion				35
Litter	63	31	71	29
Dog fouling	57	29	60	29
Depletion Britain's natural resources				27
Inner Cities		22		26
Noise	32	13	40	16

* adults over 18 years of age only
(Based on Social Trends, HMSO)

28 *Making Sense of the Census*

The following exercise is intended to be used with the software package *SCAMP-2*, the **S**chools **C**ensus **A**nalysis and **M**apping **P**ackage, available from Pebbleshore. There is a special offer on this software available to all purchasers of this book and details can be found on the inside back cover. Pebbleshore can also supply a Demonstration disk to teachers, which is fully functional but only covers the Medina District on the Isle of Wight. Both the full product and the Demo come with full installation instructions.

This exercise can also be adapted to be used without the computer software if you:

- obtain Ward boundary maps of your local area

- obtain the full printed 1991 Census data available for your local area at Ward level (Small Area Statistics)

- map the locations of all existing schools in your area.

Inevitably, it will be much more difficult to organize and more time-consuming to carry out.

The exercise involves:

- a decision on the location of a new facility

- decisions on census data and its uses (making decisions as to which data to use)

- decisions on statistical and geographical analyses of census and map data (deciding how to analyse your information)

- decisions on how best to present the data cartographically.

Decision-Making Exercise

You are asked to make a decision on the location of a new multi-purpose community building in your area. It will function as:

- a school for pupils aged 5 to 15 years between the hours of 8am and 4pm, and

- a youth club for teenagers between the ages of 14 and 17 years from 5pm to 7pm, and

- a social club for pensioners (over 65 years of age) from 8pm to 10pm.

In addition to being close to the groups it is trying to serve, the new building should try to avoid:

- areas with a large proportions of people in the higher socio-economic groups

- any areas within 250 yards of a motorway or airport

- protected areas (e.g. Country Parks, Nature Reserves)

- areas with large resident populations in communal establishments

- badly affecting the catchment areas of existing schools in the area.

Use SCAMP-2 to arrive at your decision and present a full report, including maps and diagrams, as appropriate, to justify your location and to explain how you arrived at your decision.

Method

1 Run the program Map91 and SCAMP-2.

2 First, get your **Boundary map outline**. On the screen, choose with the mouse (clicking with the left button) the *Boundary* menu, then click on *Retrieve* in the drop-down menu

3 If you are using the Demo then select *Medina Wards*. If you have the full program and CD-ROM then select your own local *County* and then *District* and then choose *Wards*. You will now have an outline map of the wards in your area (try to keep to an area no larger than 100 square kilometres). Figure 28.1 shows the boundary map for the Isle of Wight.

4 The scale around the edge should be based on the grid references (if not, choose *Display, Scale, OSGrid*) to change. Bottom left is the grid reference of your cursor position (this too, can be changed to show up to 6-figure references or OS sheet numbers).

5 Now add cartographic general detail to the map.

- Click on *Data* then, in the drop-down menu, *Retrieve Cartographic Data*. This adds roads and other features.

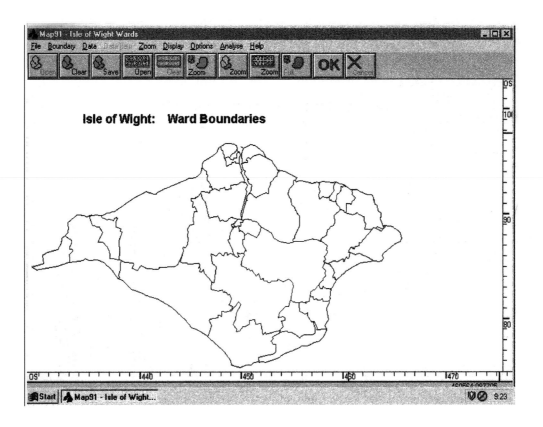

Figure 28.1

- Click on *Scale* and then *Cartographic Detail*. You will then get a screen from which you can choose which cartographic details to show and which to remove from your map, to help you decide where to locate your facility (e.g. you might want to show country parks but not lighthouses or AA telephone boxes).
- You can then display the cartographic key on screen.
- Be quite selective otherwise the cartographic detail will clutter your map!

6 Now select the **census variables** you think will be most useful and display them on your map.

- Click on *Data* then, in the drop-down menu, on *Retrieve Area Data*.
- The 17 census groups will be displayed, choose a relevant one (e.g. *Population Size and age structure*).
- Select a Data Item (e.g. *'% pensionable age'*). It will be mapped in colour and a key shown (if it is not, then click *Display* then *Zonal Key* to show the key).
- Click on *Intervals* inside the key box and you can change the classification of the data and select the most appropriate intervals to use for your data:

- if you wish, alter the *number of intervals* or classes shown on the map
- choose an appropriate *interval type* (equal, quartile, user defined or ordinal).

7 Now you can add other census data. Click on *Options* and *Map type*. Decide how to show it by choosing:

- Zonal (a choropleth map). But this is how the original data is displayed!
- Graduated rectangles
- Graduated circles

Choose rectangles or circles and then select say, *5–15 years of age*. Symbols for these will be superimposed on your choropleth of pensionable population. Figure 28.2 shows such a map for the Isle of Wight.

8 Now add **Point Data**.

- Click *Data* then *Retrieve Point Data* and select *Schools*. You will be asked to select an appropriate symbol and then all existing schools in your area will be mapped.
- If you click *Display* then *Point Data* the cursor will become a cross and if you place it over a school symbol and click you will get detailed

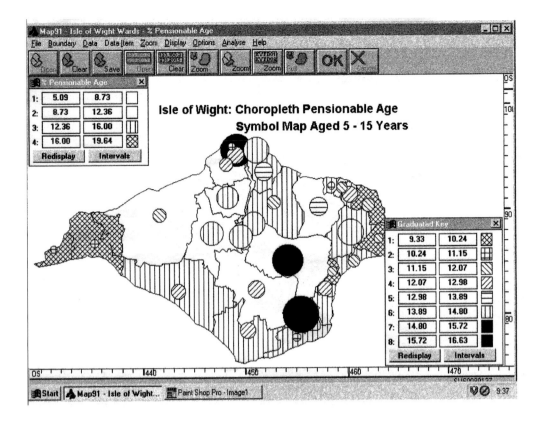

Figure 28.2

information, including the name of the school, its postcode, street name and grid reference.

9 Now **Analyse** your information. Click on *Analyse* then:

- Summary Statistics gives means, medians, standard deviations for the chosen data item
- Frequency Distribution gives a bar chart or line graph for the item
- Scatter Plot allows you to plot, say, people of pensionable age, against age 5–15 to see if they live in similar or different areas. It also calculates Spearman's Rank Correlation and Pearson's Product Moment Correlation Coefficients.

10 Repeat all the above as often as necessary, choosing appropriate data, displays and analyses for your decision-making, and then saving and/or printing your maps as you go.

11 Decide where to locate your new multi-purpose facility.

12 Now, look at its catchment area – what other schools or features are nearby?

- Click on *Display* then *Scale* then select *Metric*.

This changes the grid reference scale to a metric distance scale

- Click *Analyse* then *Points in area* then select *Circular area*:
  - place cursor over your selected site for your facility and hold mouse key down
  - drag cursor away from the point, you will see a circle appear. When your circle is about 5 km diameter measured on the scale (you decide how large a circle to draw), release the mouse key and you will get a display of the number of points (schools etc.) inside your circle, that is, all other schools within that radius or catchment of your chosen location.

13 You can also:

- measure distances between points
- measure the area of *polygons* (the Wards), or circles or rectangles
- zoom in and out
- add Text to the display (to title your map, or add a name to your site)

14 Make sure that you *Save* and *Print* whatever you need to compile your decision report. You can print in hatch shading if you do not have a colour printer.

29 Cycling in Towns: International Answers?

'The bicycle is the vehicle of a new mentality. It quietly challenges a system of values which condones dependency, wastage, inequality of mobility and daily carnage. There is every reason why cycling should be helped to enjoy another golden age.'

J McGurn

This exercise needs careful analysis of the general information provided in order to arrive at two, more localized, decisions. The ability to synthesise data from a variety of geographical scales and from different cultures and locations is an important decision-making skill. The data is real, but the specific scenarios are fictitious.

International Cycle Planning Inc.
337 Hakkai Road
Tokyo
Japan

Dear Sam,

We have another assignment for you. As our UK-based consultant on planning for cycles in towns across the globe, we would like you to analyse and report on the projects we have been instructed to research.

We have enclosed a great deal of information on cycling and cycle planning, including much on Great Britain, London and Shanghai, and, as usual, we need to have an international analysis perspective in your report, even though you are recommending on two particular European projects.

We would like:

1 A detailed analysis of the international data to persuade our clients of the need and advantages of planning for cycles in urban areas.

2 A reasoned plan for cycle facilities in the Bijlmermeer redevelopment in The Netherlands (Figure 29.7)

3 A reasoned plan for cycle facilities in the central zone of King's Lynn, Norfolk (Figures 29.5, 29.6)

4 Your assessment, for our internal use, of the reasons why your two plans may differ in character and detail.

Yours sincerely,

Yoshi Tagamuchi

Bijlmermeer is an area of honeycomb-pattern high-rise flats with lots of open spaces developed 1960–1970 as a southern suburb of Amsterdam. It has a metro line through its centre, peripheral roads and a shopping centre. Through traffic is minimal and the city authorities are now in a redevelopment phase to overcome earlier problems of access and facilities. Your task is to plan for the cycle and, if you consider it necessary, map out cycle routeways. You should describe and justify all proposals.

King's Lynn is a long-established market town and port in Norfolk containing a large number of 'Listed' historic buildings in the town centre. Your task here is to recommend cycle facilities in the central area as appropriate and, again, to plan routes for the cyclists if you think them necessary and feasible. Again, detailed plans must be justified.

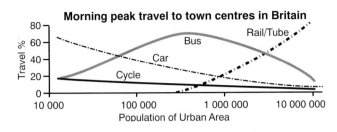

Morning peak travel to town centres in Britain

Figure 29.1

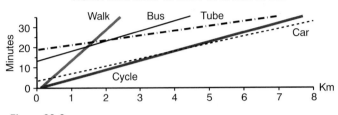

Travel time door to door in urban areas

Figure 29.2

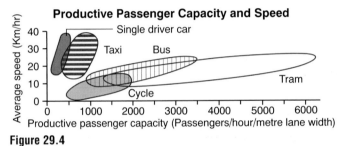

Productive Passenger Capacity and Speed

Figure 29.4

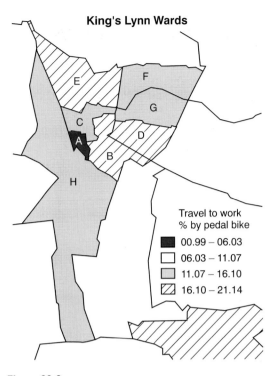

King's Lynn Wards

Travel to work
% by pedal bike

■	00.99 – 06.03
□	06.03 – 11.07
▨	11.07 – 16.10
▨	16.10 – 21.14

Figure 29.3

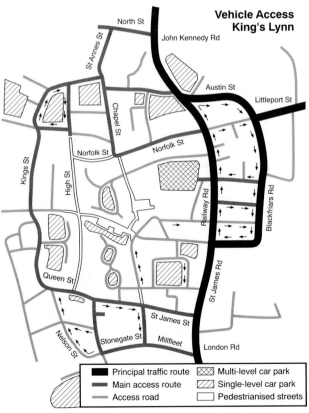

Vehicle Access King's Lynn

■	Principal traffic route	▨	Multi-level car park
▬	Main access route	▨	Single-level car park
—	Access road	□	Pedestrianised streets

Figure 29.5

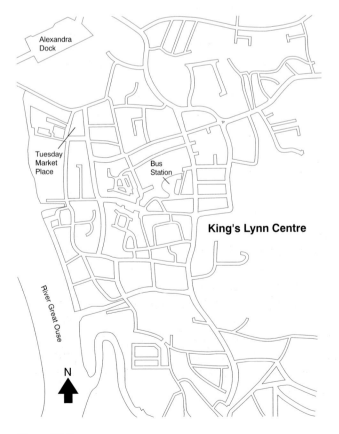

King's Lynn Centre

Figure 29.6

Figure 29.9

TRAVEL TO WORK IN BRITAIN

1: Modes of Transport 1965–1986
(Percentages)

Date	Walk	Cycle	M/Cycle	Bus	Car/Van	Rail
1965	8	12	4	32	35	6
1972	6	6	3	23	54	5
1975	7	7	3	17	59	5
1978	7	5	3	19	59	5
1986	6	6	3	11	67	5

2: Cycle Travel to Work by Income
(Percentages)

Income £	Percentage by cycle
<2000	6
<3000	8
<4000	4
<5000	5
<6000	5
<7000	4
<10 000	4
>10 000	3

3: Cycle Travel to Work by Size of Urban Area
(Percentages)

Urban Area (Population)	Percentage by cycle
London	4
Conurbations	4
100 000–1 000 000	6
3000–100 000	6
Rural <3000	7

PLANNING FOR CYCLES IN BRITAIN: LONDON 1996

1: Cycle policies in Local Plans of Boroughs
(Maximum 33)

Cycle Policy	Number of Boroughs with Policies
Encourage cycling	17
Constraints on people cycling:	
Accidents	29
Security	4
Inconvenience	14
Lack facilities/cycleways	8
Benefits of cycling:	
Social equality	7
Convenience	7
Health	16
Environment friendly	25
Economic benefit	8
Speed in London	14
Planning development for cycles	25
Integrate with public transport	6

2: London Cycle Network
(metres)

Planned 1987	Completed 1994	Percentage Completed
1 982 800	833 124	42%

Figure 29.13

Figure 29.11

VEHICLE OWNERSHIP, BRITAIN
(Percentages)

Household Type	None	Cycle only	M/Cycle	Car	>1 Car
1 person <65	63	6	2	29	1
1 person >65	92	3	0	5	0
2 persons	63	8	1	26	2
3 persons inc children	25	10	1	57	8
4 persons inc children	17	11	0	51	21
All households	39	8	2	42	9

Figure 29.10

CYCLE TRIPS BY PURPOSE OF TRIP, BRITAIN

Purpose	Percentage of Trips by Cycle		
	Age <16	Age <60	Age >60
Education	8	6	0
Shopping	11	3	4
Recreation	8	1	3
Social Visits	9	2	2
Holidays	1	0	1
Day trips	15	2	2
To/at Work	–	9	11

CYCLE TRIPS: PERCENTAGES OF ALL TRAVEL DISTANCES TAKEN BY CYCLE, BY REGION OF BRITAIN

Region	Percentage of all travel in region that is by cycle
North	0.6
Yorks/Humberside	1.3
E Midlands	1.1
E Anglia	3.2
Gtr London	0.8
Rest South East	1.1
South West	1.2
W Midlands	0.9
North West	0.6
Wales	0.5
Scotland	0.3

Figure 29.12

Bijlmermeer, Amsterdam

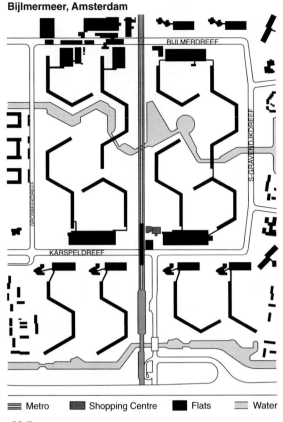

 Metro   ■ Shopping Centre   ■ Flats   ▨ Water

Figure 29.7

Transport Management in Shanghai

Shanghai Station

Nanjing St

Wusong River

Huangpu River

People's Park

Pudong Development District

Xizang St

Huaihai St

MV = Motor vehicle
NMV = Non-motor vehicle (mostly cycles)

━━ Elevated road   ▪▪▪▪▪ Segregation of MV with NMV
━━ MV road   ───── One-way traffic
▬·▬·▬ NMV road   ·········· MV and NMV contraflow
─ ─ ─ Bus only   ·········· Bus and NMV contraflow
▬▬▬▬ Passenger MV only

Source: Shanghai Urban Planning and Design Institute

Figure 29.8

Figure 29.16 Bijlmermeer

SHANGHAI URBAN TRANSPORT

1: Mode of Transport 1981–1991
(Percentages)

Year	Public Transport	Cycle	Car, Other
1981	67.7	30.5	1.8
1986	58.2	40.3	1.5
1991	53.8	43.9	2.3

2: Population, Cycles and Cars 1988
(thousands)

Cycles	Cars	Population	Cycles per 1 000 pop.	Cars per 1 000 pop.
5 600	200	12,400	445	12

3: Other Shanghai data

Metropolitan area:	6 340² km.
Population 1992	13 000 000
Person trips per day	21 000 000

Mode of trips in central urban area:
Cycle	31%
Public transport	24%
Walk	41%
Car	4%
Number of cycles in Shanghai 1993	6 516 000
Population density in urban area	25 000 persons/ km².

Figure 29.14

BIJLMERMEER REDEVELOPMENT, AMSTERDAM

1: Other data

Population Amsterdam 1991	703 000
Cycling in the Netherlands:	
All trips	29% by cycle
Travel to work trips	30% by cycle
Travel to school	60% by cycle

2: Percentage Travel by Mode in Amsterdam 1960–1980

Area	Mode	1960	1980
City Centre	bus/tram	31	40
	car	25	36
	cycle	44	24
Pre-war districts	bus/tram	22	24
	car	32	56
	cycle	46	20
Periphery	bus/tram	22	11
	car	46	78
	cycle	32	11
Whole Conurbation	bus/tram	24	17
	car	36	69
	cycle	40	14

Figure 29.15

PLANNING FOR THE CYCLE

1: To Integrate or Segregate the Cycle into City Structure?

Figure 29.19 Nelson St., King's Lynn

Integrating the Cycle	Segregating the Cycle
Modifying existing road and pathway system	New, physically separate cycle ways
Cheaper, minimal construction	Expensive, lot of construction
Easier in old towns	Easiest in new towns
May disrupt current vehicle provisions	Fits comprehensive vehicle planning
Routes may be minimal – lines on roads/paths	Discrete, constructed routes
Cycle routes on roads/paths can confuse other users	Clear routes
Follows existing roads, therefore good routes	May not be ideal cyclist's route A to B
May induce cyclists to use paths without cycleways	Segregated, so clear use
Not so safe, as shared with other vehicles/pedestrians	Very safe, including child cyclists
Commuter-oriented, saves time in urban areas	Recreational cyclist-oriented
New signs and road/path markings needed	Can use old unused road/rail lines
Can conflict with pedestrians/traffic	No conflict
Best for experienced cyclists	Safe for inexperienced cyclists
Uses human energy only	Uses human energy only
Healthy for cyclists	Healthy for cyclists
Limited use of new space	Entirely uses new or re-used space
No noise/pollution created	No noise/pollution created
Cyclists suffer from vehicle pollution	No pollution problems
No need for large parking areas	No need for large parking areas
Can be widespread, but aesthetically intrusive	Often few routes and pleasant
May not be continuous	Continuous

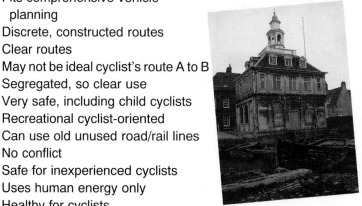

Figure 29.20 Custom's House, c.1683, King's lynn

2: Location factors to take into account

Land use – origin points usually residential

Short distance travel only

New cycleways require access to continuous linear route and construction possibilities

Integrated cycleways have to use/adapt existing routes and facilities

Often problem of lack of complete, continuous route if adapting existing facilities

Hierarchy possible – into town centre, to other destinations

Destinations largely for work, school, recreation

Level terrain best, lack of hills

Access to other modes e.g. trains, buses can be useful

Barriers of rivers, main roads/motorways (high speed traffic), tunnels, very steep gradients

Routes internal to residential areas easiest, more difficult in established town centres

Integrating with traffic easiest and safest when traffic speeds slower than 25 mph

Intersections, poor road surfaces and parked cars particular hazards

Probably safest where number of cyclists/cycle owners is high (more visible form of travel)

Need a social/cultural acceptance of this form of transport?

Figure 29.21 Tuesday, Market Place, King's Lynn

1: General town data

Population	34 000
Percentage population without car	40%
Percentage travel to work by cycle	20%

2: Ward data (Figure 29.3)

Ward	Population	Percentage Travel to Work by Cycle
A (Town Centre)	1989	4.9
B	3874	17.3
C	2917	14.8
D	7382	17.1
E	4210	21.1
F	6775	11.8
G	4030	11.3
H	3774	12.7

Figure 29.18

Figure 29.17

30 · *Renewal Of Sea Defences in North East Norfolk*

The following exercise is loosely based on an analysis carried out by North Norfolk District Council using the Anglian Water's pilot study of building 600 m of sea-wall with a design life of 60 years. Cost-Benefit Analysis was at the heart of the decision-making process.

You are provided with background information and illustrations, together with two analysis tables and you are asked to decide: **Should the sea defences in this part of Norfolk be replaced?**

Specifically, you need to address the following questions in your final report. Each should be supported from the evidence and your reasoning should be shown. *Your arguments must be based on the data and analyses in the exercise and should NOT use the 'What Really Happened?' information which is given at the end of the exercise.*

Decision-Making Exercise

1 For how many of the 60 years might there be a benefit?

2 What do you see as the major shortcomings of the scheme?

COST-BENEFIT DATA CALCULATION

(1) CAPITAL COST

Cost of building and maintaining 600 m of sea wall (for 60 years) @ £2023 per m	£ _____	**(A)**

(2) BENEFIT OF SEA-WALL (COST OF FLOODING)

(a) Capital benefits

880 ha arable land @ £6200/ha	£	
62 ha grassland @ £3700/ha	£	
Less value of above land for summer grazing post-flood	£ −2 355 000 (Deduct)	
24 farms @ £79 500	£	
156 houses @ £27 800	£	
310 cottages @ £17 800	£	
92 chalets @ £9000	£	
147 caravans @ £3900	£	
Value of dwellings' contents	£ 2 357 900	
Road rebuilding	£ 1 200 000	
Total Capital Benefit	£ _____	**(B)**

(b) Annual benefit

Additional travel If direct route Stalham–Sea Palling/Horsey is cut, alternative route is an extra 17 km @ 15p per km 200 journeys per day, 365 days	£	
Loss of income from flooded arable and dairy land	£ 470 840	
Total Annual Benefit	£ _____	**(C)**

Figure 30.1

Figure 30.2

COST-BENEFIT ANALYSIS

(1)   **Total Capital Cost of Scheme**   £ millions

                                                                               £   **(A)**

(2)

Build Year 1984	BENEFITS (£millions)		COST (£millions)
			£
1994 Yr 10	Capital benefit of defences (B)	£	Cost with inflation at 5% p.a. $(A \times 1.05)^{10}$ (A1)
	Total annual benefits for remaining 50 yrs $(C \times 50)$	£	
	TOTAL (D1)	£	**C:B RATIO** (D1/A1)
2009 Yr 35	Capital benefit of defences (B)	£	£
			Cost with inflation at 5% p.a. $(A \times 1.05)^{25}$ (A2)
	Total annual benefits for remaining 35 yrs $(C \times 35)$	£	
	TOTAL (D2)	£	**C:B RATIO** (D2/A2)
2042 Yr 58	Capital benefit of defences (B)	£	£
			Cost with inflation at 5% p.a. $(A \times 1.05)^{58}$ (A3)
	Total annual benefits for remaining 2 yrs $(C \times 2)$	£	
	TOTAL (D3)	£	**C:B RATIO** (D3/A3)
2043 Yr 59	Capital benefit of defences (B)	£	£
			Cost with inflation at 5% p.a. $(A \times 1.05)^{59}$ (A4)
	Total annual benefits for remaining 1 yr $(C \times 1)$	£	
	TOTAL (D4)	£	**C:B RATIO** (D4/A4)
2044 Yr 60	Capital benefit of defences (B)	£	£
			Cost with inflation at 5% p.a. $(A \times 1.05)^{60}$ (A5)
	Total annual benefits for remaining 0 yrs $(C \times 0)$	£ 00.00	
	TOTAL (D5)	£	**C:B RATIO** (D5/A5)

NB It is normal to discount the benefits by 5% p.a. rather than increase the costs, but the latter is a simpler calculation and has been adopted for this exercise.

NOTE:

- *The figures are based on 1984 costs, when the analysis was undertaken. An assumption is made that inflation is constant at 5% and that the costs increase at that rate. Thus services costing £100 in 1984 would cost £105 in 1985 (£100 × 1.05) and £110.25 in 1986 (£105 × 1.05), etc.*

- *While the cost:benefit ratio (inaccurately described, as it is really a benefit:cost ratio!) is above 1.0, the benefit of the defences outweigh their costs.*

3 Based on your cost-benefit analyses, should the defences be rebuilt?

4 What other benefits, other than those costed, might occur from building the defences?

5 What other losses, other than those costed, might be involved if the defences are not built?

Two tables (Figures 30.1, 30.2) are provided to enable you to carry out your own Cost-Benefit Analysis. You should work through the figures and complete the tables first, before further investigation. Figure 30.1 generates the data for the CBA, Figure 30.2 carries out the CBA.

Background Information

1 **The coast of north-east Norfolk is particularly subject to storm attack**. There are several reasons for this:

- The North Sea is funnel shaped (Figure 30.3), so that when the tide sweeps in down the North Sea it becomes constricted as the sea narrows. The water piles up and the height difference between high and low tide (the *tidal range*) increases southwards. East Anglia protrudes into the North Sea, causing it to narrow rapidly from c. 300 km to less than 200 km, emphasizing the funnelling effect.
- In addition to high water caused by the tide, water is also pushed southwards down the North Sea by north winds. As there is no land between north Norfolk and the Arctic, there is no hindrance to this process. This factor is particularly important when a depression passes from Britain to Germany, Denmark or southern Scandinavia. In the rear part of the depression, winds blow from north to south and the deeper the depression, the more strongly the winds blow, causing storms that drive more water southwards into the North Sea funnel. The protruding north coast of Norfolk bears the brunt of these storms and is particularly vulnerable at high tide during a storm.
- This effect is compounded by the fact that water rises as air pressure decreases, the rise being greater, the deeper the depression.

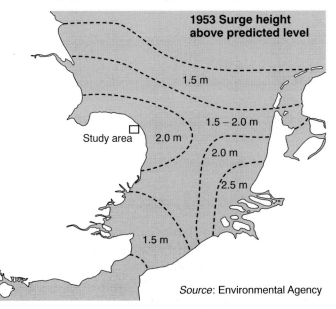

Figure 30.3

Source: Environmental Agency

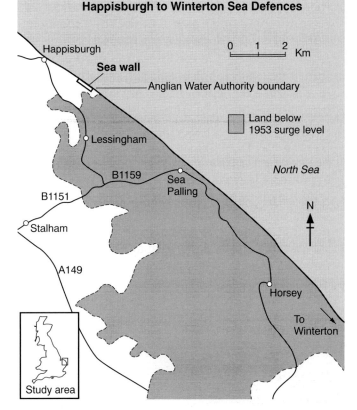

Figure 30.4

- Over the last 100 years, records show that sea-level around the East Anglian coast has risen by 150 mm.
- Given that global warming will lead to higher sea-levels (estimates varying between 0.5 and 2.0 m) and increased storminess, the vulnerability of the area will be further increased.

2 **Storms attack the cliffs of north Norfolk and contribute to their retreat**. Between Happisburgh and Winterton, 6,000 ha of land is at, or close to, sea level, including part of the Norfolk Broads, and is protected only by a single dune line, 14 km long and varying between 30 and 100 metres wide (Figure 30.4). At normal high tides, the sea is often higher than the land behind the dune line. Four or five storm surges each year can be a metre or more higher than predicted. On 31 January 1953 a storm surge coincided with high spring tide, giving water levels 2.4 m above those predicted.

3 **The sand dune is vital to protect the land behind from flooding**. The coast of Norfolk is in retreat and has been at least since historical times. The former hamlet of Shipden, recorded in

the Domesday Book, now lies somewhere out to sea north of Cromer pier. As the cliffed coast has retreated, so the dune line has moved southwards also. On the foreshore in front of the dune line near Happisburgh, the remains of the medieval settlement of Eccles are sometimes exposed (Figure 30.5). The dune line retreated southwards over a landscape of meadows and river channels. The present dune line, therefore, has a varied substrate. In 1938, a severe storm exploited the weaker river sediments asssociated with the Hundred Stream near Horsey and undermined the dune line, causing extensive flooding, covering 3,000 ha. In 1953 another severe storm caused a breach at Sea Palling, flooding an area of 490 ha and causing seven deaths.

Figure 30.6

Figure 30.5

4 **Concrete sea defences were built** between Happisburgh and Winterton in the years after 1953. These comprised a series of steps surmounted by a concave wall and then by an apron (Figure 30.6). The concave wall was designed to throw back storm waves with the minimum of scouring of the beach, and the apron was intended to stop high waves eroding the front of the dune line. For the most part, this form of sea defence was successful, but in some places it was less so. The source of sand to maintain and build up the dune line was the beach and the sand was transferred by the wind. Normally the wind would blow sand around on the beach and some would become trapped by vegetation at the foot of the dune. Over time, the amount of trapped sand would build up and so cause the dune to grow. However, the concrete structures broke the natural link between the beach and the dune and caused the latter to degrade in places (Figure 30.7).

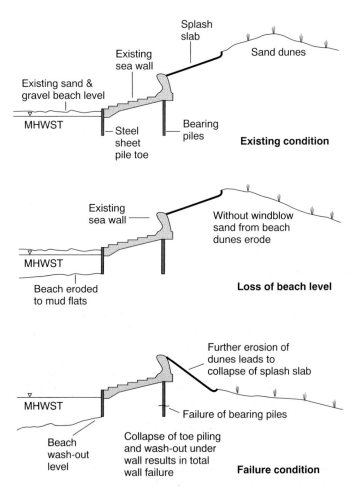

Figure 30.7 Sequence of Failure of Sea Wall

5 **The dune line is also becoming more vulnerable.** The beach tends to lose sand to the offshore by natural processes, particularly during storms when the beach can be lowered temporarily by up to 2.0 m. In places the scouring has cut into the clay beneath the beach,

threatening to undermine the defences, but also creating steeper beach profiles making the beach more vulnerable to further attack. In the long term such losses were balanced by an input from the north-west along the coast by longshore drift. However, as coastal defences have been developed along the coast, the input from longshore drift has been severely diminished. The net loss from the beach now amounts to 400,000 m^3 per year. In 1984, Anglian Water estimated that within five years the defences would start to be undermined and within 50 years the reduced longshore drift and the scouring during storms would cause a total loss of the beach and, thereby, the dunes, as the beach is the source for the dune sand.

6 **The structures built after the 1953 flood had a design life of 30 years**, a normal procedure in civil engineering at the time. Thus, by the 1990s, the sea defences, though still largely in place and functioning, were life-expired and there were areas where their effectiveness were already giving cause for concern. Given the geomorphological and meteorological situations outlined above, and the estimated effects of global warming, further severe storms, damage and flooding are not so much a possibility, but an inevitability. Obviously a decision needed to be taken whether or not to replace the defences.

7 A Cost-Benefit pilot study was carried out by Anglian Water, now part of the Environmental Agency, to establish the cost of building 600 m of sea-wall with a design life of 60 years at Cart Gap, near Happisburgh.

Your CBA is based on the results of this pilot study. The tables below should be compiled after reading the following notes:

• The result of the pilot study was a cost of £2,023 per metre at 1984 prices. For every year's delay costs were presumed to rise by 5%. Such a wall would preserve the integrity of the current structures and prevent flooding, but would not address the loss of sand affecting the beach and the dunes.

• The costs used below are only those that can be quantified and no account is taken of other matters such as the human cost of losing homes, or farm businesses built up over years, or the effect on the holiday industry if the beach deteriorates.

• Benefits comprise *capital benefits* and *annual benefits*. The benefits come from
  • saving the capital loss of land, farms, houses, etc. (capital benefit) and
  • saving the loss of income and costs such as extra long journeys round the flooded area (annual benefit).

• The reasoning is as follows. If the defences were built in 1984 and a storm occurred in 1994, that would have caused flooding if the defences had not been built, then the benefit is *not* losing the land, farms, houses, (*capital benefit*) and *not* having to pay out for loss of income, (*annual benefit*) for the remaining 50 years of the life of the defences. However, the benefits have to be balanced against a presumed increase in the value of the defences due to inflation.

• Both the costs and the benefits are based on the assumption that flooding would be a wholly negative experience. Obviously, much hardship and personal loss would be involved and should not be underestimated, but there could be long-term benefits. The large area of shallow open water in the new embayment that would be created could provide a safe haven for water sports, or might also stimulate developments in the local fishing industry.

What Really Happened?

For a number of reasons, including the failure to maintain the beach, rebuilding of the sea-wall was rejected. A more ambitious plan was adopted that involved protection work along the present sea-wall, recharging the beach to make good the sand losses and a series of 16 offshore artificial reefs to break the storms and stop the loss of sand from the beach. By 1997, four of the reefs had been constructed. Sand is building up behind the reefs, but there is scouring of the beach opposite the gaps between the reefs. Eventually it is envisaged that there will be a series of salients behind the reefs separated by shallow bays.

Reefs were chosen because the cause of the beach scouring was not due to the effects of tidal currents, which could have been controlled by fish-tail breakwaters, but by high waves oblique to the coast and storm surges. The energy of the waves and surges needed to be reduced before the beach was reached. Also, it is envisaged that the reefs scheme will allow longshore drift to continue, thus avoiding starving beaches further along the coast.

31 Opening up a Sand and Gravel Quarry

Sand and gravel are particularly important building materials. The demand is particularly for gravel, as it is less plentiful than sand. Often sand will occur without gravel, but gravel mostly occurs in association with sand.

Decision-Making Exercise

In this scenario, you are asked to take on the role of a geomorphologist advising a quarrying company on the feasibility and profitability of a particular area for extracting sand and gravel. You are provided with:

- Some background information.

- An extract from the Geological Survey map TM 02 around Colchester (Figure 31.1).

- Borehole data for thickness of deposits and overburden for boreholes shown on the map (Figure 31.2).

- A table for you to calculate the standard deviation of the sand and gravel deposits (Figure 31.3).

- A table for you to calculate the standard deviation of the overburden (Figure 31.4).

- A table for calculating the profitability of the proposed extraction area (Figure 31.5).

Figure 31.2

THICKNESSES OF OVERBURDEN AND MINERAL (SAND AND GRAVEL)		
Borehole no.	Thickness of overburden (x_o)	Thickness of mineral (x_m)
	Metres	Metres
14*	2.4	3.5
48*	3.4	0.0
49	4.3	4.6
50	3.4	2.1
51	3.7	3.7
52	3.7	3.7
53	3.0	8.2
54*	4.0	0.0
55	2.7	5.5
56	2.1	3.7
57	2.7	4.3
58	2.7	4.6
59	3.0	4.6
60	4.6	3.7
61	5.8	3.7
62	3.7	3.0
63	2.1	7.9
64	2.7	5.5
65	1.5	5.5
66	1.2	4.6
67	2.1	6.4
	Σ	Σ
	M_o	M_m

* Not shown on map
M = mean

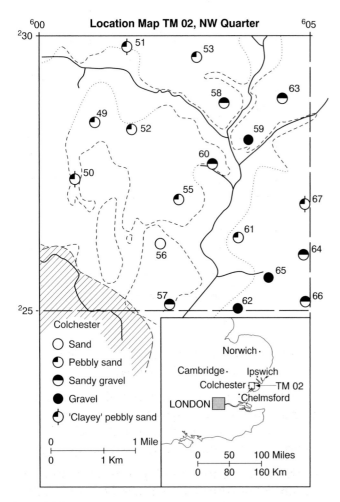

Location Map TM 02, NW Quarter

Colchester

○ Sand
◔ Pebbly sand
⊖ Sandy gravel
● Gravel
◓ 'Clayey' pebbly sand

0   1 Mile
0   1 Km

Norwich
Cambridge · Ipswich
Colchester — TM 02
LONDON · Chelmsford

0   50   100 Miles
0   80   160 Km

Figure 31.1

Use the information and your calculations of *standard deviations* and *potential profitability* to decide:

Is the evidence strong enough for you to advise the quarrying company to apply for planning permission to extract sand and gravel in this area?

Specifically, you should address, with reasons and specific evidence, the following questions in your final report:

CALCULATIONS FOR MINERAL (SAND AND GRAVEL)

Borehole no.	Thickness of mineral (x_m)	$(M_m - x_m)$	$(M_m - x_m)^2$
	Metres		
14*	3.5		
48*	0.0		
49	4.6		
50	2.1		
51	3.7		
52	3.7		
53	8.2		
54*	0.0		
55	5.5		
56	3.7		
57	4.3		
58	4.6		
59	4.6		
60	3.7		
61	3.7		
62	3.0		
63	7.9		
64	5.5		
65	5.5		
66	4.6		
67	6.4		
		Σ	Σ
	M_m		

Standard deviation of thickness $= \sigma_m = \sqrt{\dfrac{\sum (M_m - x_m)^2}{n-1}} =$

(M = mean)

Mean thickness of mineral (M_m) _____ m

Maximum thickness, 95% probability $(M_m + 2\sigma)$ _____ m

Minimum thickness, 95% probability $(M_m - 2\sigma)$ _____ m

Figure 31.3

CALCULATIONS FOR OVERBURDEN

Borehole no.	Thickness of overburden (x_o)	$(M_o - x_o)$	$(M_o - x_o)^2$
	Metres		
14*	2.4m		
48*	3.4		
49	4.3		
50	3.4		
51	3.7		
52	3.7		
53	3.0		
54*	4.0		
55	2.7		
56	2.1		
57	2.7		
58	2.7		
59	3.0		
60	4.6		
61	5.8		
62	3.7		
63	2.1		
64	2.7		
65	1.5		
66	1.2		
67	2.1		
	Σ		Σ
	M_o		

Figure 31.4

Standard deviation of thickness $= \sigma_o = \sqrt{\dfrac{\sum (M_o - x_o)^2}{n-1}} =$

(M = mean)

Mean thickness of overburden (M_o) _____ m

Maximum thickness, 95% probability $(M_o + 2\sigma)$ _____ m

Minimum thickness, 95% probability $(M_o - 2\sigma)$ _____ m

1 Would you advise your client to apply for permission to quarry in this area?

2 The calculations take no account of the quality of the mineral body in terms of gravel content. Therefore, which general areas (NW, NE, SE) would you concentrate on to site your quarry?

3 For the areas identified in (2), bearing in mind the ratio of overburden to mineral (Figure 31.2), which area would you most favour?

4 The north-west area is reasonably open, has relatively few houses and heavy clay soils, but poorer gravel resources. The north-east part of the area has more housing, better roads, a railway and a reservoir. To the south-east the area has better agricultural land, has less housing and poorer roads. If you were now a local planner, who has to take a wider variety of factors into account before granting planning permission, which of these areas would you favour for quarrying?

ANALYSIS OF POTENTIAL PROFITABILITY

The data generated so far relates to the whole area shown on the map (5 km × 5 km), whereas a quarry is not likely to be more than 0.5 km × 0.5 km, but the data can be used to give a good indication of the variations in thickness of the sand and gravel and the overburden in the area.

The maximum profit obviously occurs when the mineral is at a maximum thickness and the overburden at a minimum, but it is important to know if the quarry is still likely to be profitable when the mineral is at a minimum and the overburden thick.

For ease of calculation, work:
(a) to two decimal places only and
(b) in millions e.g. 1 500 000 = 1.5.

(1)   Greatest profit
Area of quarry, 500 m x 500 m   = _____ million m^2 (i)
Minimum thickness of overburden (Fig. 31.4)   = _____ m   (ii)
Volume of overburden, minimum   = _____ million m^3 (i × ii)

     Removal cost at £2.00 per m^3 £ (millions) _____   (a)

Area of quarry   = _____ million m^2
Maximum thickness of mineral (Fig. 31.3)   = _____ m
Volume of mineral, maximum   = _____ million m^3

     Extraction costs at £1.50 per m^3 £ (millions) _____   (b)
     Selling price at £4.50 per m^3 £ (millions) _____   (c)

Profit (+)/Loss (−)   (c − (a+b))   **£ (millions) _____**

(2)   Least profit
Area of quarry   = _____ million m^2
Maximum thickness of overburden (Fig. 31.4)   = _____ m
Volume of overburden, maximum   = _____ million m^3

     Removal cost at £2.00 per m^3 £ (millions) _____

Area of quarry   = _____ million m^2
Minimum thickness of mineral (Fig. 31.3)   = _____ m
Volume of mineral, minimum   = _____ million m^3

     Extraction costs at £1.50 per m^3 £ (millions) _____
     Selling price at £4.50 per m^3 £ (millions) _____

Profit (+)/Loss (−)   **£ (millions) _____**

(3)   Average profit
Area of quarry   = _____ million m^2
Mean thickness of overburden (Fig. 31.4)   = _____ m
Volume of overburden, mean   = _____ million m^3

     Removal cost at £2.00 per m^3 £ (millions) _____

Area of quarry   = _____ million m^2
Mean thickness of mineral (Fig. 31.3)   = _____ m
Volume of mineral, mean   = _____ million m^3

     Extraction costs at £1.50 per m^3 £ (millions) _____
     Selling price at £4.50 per m^3 £ (millions) _____

Profit (+)/Loss (−)   **£ (millions) _____**

Figure 31.5

Background Information

- In Britain, virtually all the gravel extracted is of fluvial origin, laid down in cold periods during the Pleistocene as outwash from glaciers or by periglacial rivers. Even sea-dredged aggregate is mostly of this origin, deposited on the sea bed by rivers when the sea-level was lower during the cold periods. Periglacial gravels are usually a better resource, as the outwash gravels are more likely to include silts and clays and so require more washing before leaving the quarry. In England, the main sources of periglacial gravels are ancestors of our rivers and terraces associated with our current rivers, such as the Thames, Medway, Severn and Trent. The ancestor of the Thames flowed from the Henley area, past Watford, Hertford, Chelmsford, Colchester and Ipswich. For much of the course, the gravels are buried beneath till of the Anglian glaciation and other deposits. Whilst these gravels are generally of high quality and occur close to areas of great demand, the financial viability of extracting them involves balancing the cost of removing the overburden against the value of the resource.

- *Overburden* is the material that needs to be removed in order to get at the sand and gravel – the more there is, the more expensive is the quarrying.

- A sand and gravel company might look at a large area to decide its potential and then buy land for quarrying operations within that area. One source of information is the reports of the Mineral Assessment Unit of the Geological Survey. These describe the thickness of the overburden, the thickness of the sand and gravel and its quality in terms its sand or gravel content. In the example, a sand and gravel company might consider the area to the north-east of Colchester (Figure 31.1) where borehole investigations show that sand and gravel occur, although they are beneath overburden. A major problem is that both the overburden and the sand and gravel are of variable thickness, so land bought for quarrying might have thick overburden and little mineral resource or vice-versa. So, the quarry company needs to look at a best and a worst scenario. This can be done by finding the mean thickness of the overburden and of the mineral and applying two standard deviations to both. This can give the worst and best scenarios at a 95% probability.

- In a wider context, it should be borne in mind that these gravels occur in areas where the land is of good agricultural and scenic quality. Thus a planning authority would need to balance:
  - the area's need for gravel and
  - the economic case put forward by the quarry owners against a wider variety of factors, including the damage to local agriculture and the loss of scenic amenity.

32 International Trade and Development

Development is essentially a matter of raising the overall productivity of an economy, so as to permit continuing and widespread improvements in general welfare
B. Higgins 1979

This seemingly straightforward statement hides the complex reality for poor countries trying to escape the poverty trap. In the years following the Second World War, many Third World countries broke free from colonialism and there was great optimism about their development potential. However, this optimism gradually receded as relative stagnation set in and, by the 1970s and 1980s, they were faced with the even bigger problems of an energy crisis and a debt crisis.

With some notable exceptions, it became apparent that poverty was more widespread and deep-rooted than had been thought and authors like Reitsma and Kleinpenning, in their book *The Third World in Perspective* began to talk of the problems of *'vicious cycles of poverty'* (Figure 32.1). Breaking out of these cycles was made more difficult by the high rates of population growth experienced by these countries, which affected all of their actions, and the difficulties of taking direct action in the only three major ways possible, to improve their lot:

1 **Improved rates of growth in Gross Domestic Product (GDP)** to develop self-sustaining economies

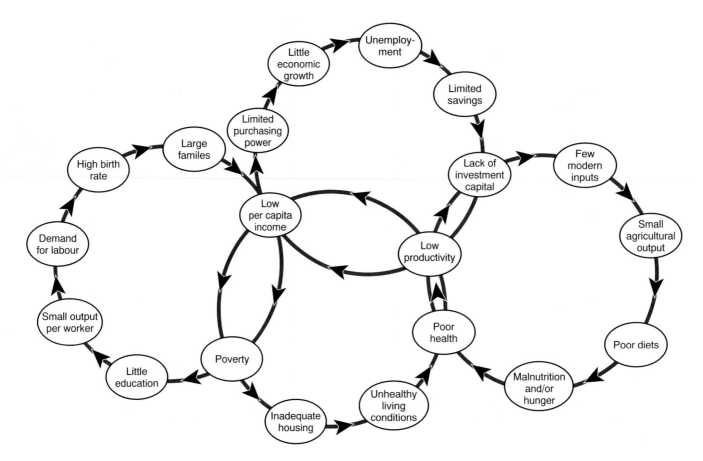

Figure 32.1

2 **Outside financial aid**, which could only ever be a temporary measure to help in the crisis period before developing self-sustaining economies and improving GDP.

3 **Exporting products in international trade**, which initially meant the commodity trades developed during the colonial period, but was intended to afford protection by import-substitution.

Decision-Making Exercise

You are provided with:

- Background context material

- Figures from the World Bank on a series of countries, for the periods 1980–1988 (Figure 32.2) and 1980–1993 (Figure 32.3), including

  - Gross Domestic Product
  - Export Trade
  - Population Growth
  - World Bank Categories based on each country's state income

You should also use any knowledge you have of the countries listed, to help your analysis. You are asked to decide:

1 What are the apparent relationships between Population Growth, GDP, Export Trade and World Bank Category?

2 How far did these relationships evolve between the two periods (and look at which particular countries changed their World Bank standing)?

3 In the light of the contextual material and using the tables, identify your own *Development Categories*, clusters or groups of similar countries and explain your classification.

4 Identify, and explain, any countries that appear anomolous or exceptional in your classification.

5 Justify your *Development Categories* – do they open up any new perspectives in the analysis of development?

6 Finally, if you were engaged as an adviser on the strategies to adopt to develop these countries, and using your *Development Categories*, would your advice be to concentrate on export trade?

GDP, TRADE, POPULATION AND WORLD BANK CATEGORIES IN SELECTED COUNTRIES 1980–1988

Country	GDP % p.a Growth	Export Trade % change p.a.	Population Growth % p.a.	World Bank Category
Ethiopia	1.4	−0.7	2.9	Low Income
Tanzania	2.0	−5.4	3.5	
Malawi	2.6	3.3	3.4	
Zambia	0.7	−3.7	3.7	
China	10.3	11.9	1.3	
India	5.2	4.7	2.2	
Indonesia	5.1	2.9	2.1	
Philippines	0.1	0.4	2.5	Lower Middle Income
Morocco	4.2	5.0	2.7	
Thailand	6.0	11.3	1.9	
Jamaica	0.6	−4.5	1.5	
Tunisia	3.4	3.0	2.5	
Mexico	0.5	5.5	2.2	
Malaysia	4.6	9.4	2.6	
Brazil	2.9	6.0	2.2	
South Africa	1.3	0.2	2.3	Upper Middle Income
Argentina	−0.2	0.1	1.4	
Algeria	3.5	3.4	3.1	
Venezuela	0.9	0.4	2.8	
Korea, Rep	9.9	14.7	1.2	
Singapore	5.7	7.3	1.1	High Income
Hong Kong	7.3	12.3	1.5	

Source: World Bank Development Report 1990

Figure 32.2

GDP, TRADE, POPULATION AND WORLD BANK CATEGORIES IN SELECTED COUNTRIES 1980–1993

Country	GDP % p.a Growth	Export Trade % change p.a.	Population Growth % p.a.	World Bank Category
Ethiopia	1.8	−2.2	2.7	Low Income
Tanzania	3.6	−0.4	3.2	
Malawi	3.0	2.1	3.4	
Zambia	0.9	−2.6	3.7	
China	9.6	11.5	1.4	
India	5.2	7.0	2.0	
Philippines	1.4	3.4	2.3	Lower Middle Income
Morocco	3.7	3.9	2.2	
Jamaica	2.3	2.1	0.9	
Tunisia	3.7	7.2	2.3	
Algeria	2.1	3.0	2.7	
Indonesia	5.8	6.7	1.7	
South Africa	0.9	5.4	2.4	Upper Middle Income
Argentina	0.8	3.2	1.4	
Venezuela	2.1	1.7	2.5	
Korea, Rep.	9.1	12.3	1.1	
Mexico	1.6	5.4	2.3	
Malaysia	6.2	12.6	2.5	
Brazil	2.1	5.2	2.0	
Thailand	8.2	15.5	1.7	
Singapore	6.9	12.7	1.1	High Income
Hong Kong	6.5	15.8	1.1	

Source: World Bank Development Report 1995

Figure 32.3

Background Information

- Adam Smith advocated *Free Trade* in the 18th century and David Ricardo developed the *Theory of Comparative Advantage* which states that all countries should specialise in what they do best and exchange trade with other countries who do other things better

- Australia and Japan are countries where trade *did* provide an engine for growth.

- Colonialism generally distorted the simple trade/development idea.

- In the twentieth century, protectionism and world wars reduced the possibilities of developing export trades.

- After the Second World War, efforts were made to help global trade:
  - The United Nations encouraged trade between countries
  - The World Bank and International Monetary Fund provided help
  - GATT, the General Agreement on Tariffs and Trade was intended to help

- Between 1950 and 1993, the dollar value of world trade increased more than 80 times, but the relative position of non-industrial states worsened.

- The Asian economies prospered best through trade in the earlier period.

- With the collapse of Communism and an international debt crisis, the late 1980s saw a reduction in protectionist policies and more prospects for trade.

- In 1995, GATT became WTO, the World Trade Organisation, with 122 members (GATT had 23 initially) aiming for 'open, fair and undistorted competition ... a particular responsibility to help developing countries and countries in transition from command to free market economies'.

- In global terms, the emphasis on trade increased during the 1990s.

- The term *Third World* was originally intended to distinguish a third grouping as opposed to the capitalist and communist blocs. The break-up of the communist group has made the term less applicable today.

- In 1981 the World Bank classified countries according to their level of income:
  - Low Income (34 countries)
  - Lower-Middle-Income (39)
  - Upper-Middle-Income (21)
  - High-Income Oil Exporters (4)
  - Industrial Market Economies (19)
  - East European Non-Market Economies (8)

The categories may not be as applicable now, as they were during the 1980s.

33 SimCity 2000: Building a New Town

Decision-making and Simulations

The software package *SimCity 2000* provides a powerful opportunity to investigate a variety of approaches to the building of cities and to investigate geographical factors and theories of urban structure and development. System simulations look at *real-world* phenomena within a computerised model that is governed by rules of behaviour. One of the most famous early examples was the game of *Life*, which simulated evolution through *cellular automata* – a spatial grid in which each cell reacted automatically according to rules based on the changes occurring in adjacent cells.

SimCity is based on the same idea, each cell of the map reacts according to the changes you make in other cells, the level of effect depending on the basic geographical concept of distance *decay* (influence declines with distance). Each cell, or block, is influenced by a number of elements of the urban environment – buildings, land-use, land value, traffic, population, pollution or crime, and each element interacts with the others (for example, industrial development may increase employment, but may also make the area less attractive for living in and may reduce land values). Every decision you make to alter the area costs money and you must be able to finance your construction, just as in the real world.

Computer simulations allow us to try 'what-if?' decision-making modelling – as we learn the rules of interaction, all of which are based on real factors or theories, we can build better and faster by trying out the possibilities we identify. The SimCity simulation is based on accepted urban theories – for example, the *Arcologies* you can build when your town becomes large are based on Paolo Soleri's ideas on *Arcosanti* or, cities within cities (high-density buildings with all city functions). It also works in *real-time* so that, even when you do nothing, micro-simulations are going on in the background. There is no 'correct' result – learning from doing is paramount.

Simulations like this encourage imaginative thinking, decision-making skills of all kinds, use of knowledge and interdisciplinary approaches and all in a fun environment.

Decision-Making Exercise

You have been engaged as an urban planner to design and plan for the building of a New Town. You also have to identify the factors that are likely to influence its growth. You are shown how to create a physical landscape in which you must build, and are given the rules of the exercise and information on the reports you must provide. You will be working with human, economic, political and survival factors.

STEP ONE: CREATE THE PHYSICAL LANDSCAPE

1. When you first run SimCity 2000 you are presented with a list of options:

> Load Saved City
>
> Start New City
>
> Edit New Map
>
> Load Scenario
>
> Quit

Use the first command only to retrieve your city if you have saved it and come back to it. It you use the *Start New City* command the program will generate a random physical landscape, which may not be the kind we want. The *Load Scenario* command will start up a complex existing city scenario.

So, we need to use the *Edit New Map* command,

as we want to control the kind of landscape we will use in our simulation.

If the exercise is being done by a group or class, it would probably help if a single physical landscape was created, so that all participants begin from the same baseline scenario.

2. Clicking on the *Edit New Map* button will open a screen with a base map and the *Terrain Toolbar*, (Figure 33.1), which we will now use to create our desired landscape.

3. Click on the *Coast* icon at the top of the toolbar to include a saltwater ocean coastline.

4. Click on the *River* icon to include a freshwater river on your map.

5. Use the *Sliders* below these icons (click and drag) to set the levels of *mountains*, *water* and *trees* in your landscape. It is suggested that the sliders are set at about 25%, 10% and 30% respectively.

6. Now click on the *Make* icon to generate your new landscape. If you are not satisfied, go back and start again. If it looks fine, then move on to more detailed landscaping (do not use the *Make* button after using the other tools, as you will lose your detailed elements).

7. The icons below the *Make* button add detail:

8. *Raise* or *Lower terrain* by clicking on the icon and on the map, dragging for wider effect – aim for some higher land, but not too much (about 35% maximum).

9. *Stretch* or *Level terrain* by using the next icons, if your high points are too extreme.

10. *Raise* or *Lower Sea Level* next – do not use the *Raise Sea Level* icon unless you want a really difficult landscape!

11. *Place Water* (for ponds or lakes) or *Place Stream* (as tributaries to your river) if you wish, but do not have too much water around. If you do this over hillsides you will get waterfalls.

12. *Place Tree* (individual trees) or *Place Forest* if you wish to add to the wooded areas. Avoid too much.

13. When you are happy with the landscape, click on the *Done* icon and you will be asked to give your city a name (use your own name), select a level of difficulty (select *Easy*) and a starting

date for your simulation (select *1900*). When you click here on *Done*, you will begin your simulation.

14. Aim for a physical landscape with a coastline and a river roughly across the map's central portion, some high but more lowland, at least one heavily wooded area and not too many water areas.

15. After creating the landscape you MUST NOT use the *Terrain Toolbar* again.

STEP TWO: BUILD THE NEW TOWN
If you followed Step One, you will now be running the simulation.

If you are using a previously saved landscape, then you will need to run the program and then select the *Load Saved City* icon in the opening sequence, and choose the saved city that you need.

The Task: Your task is to build your New Town from the year 1900, as fast as possible. You need first to create residential areas for people to live in, industrial areas for work and commercial areas for shopping and business. All will need to be supplied with power (through power plants and power lines), transportation links to enable them to move about and water to be supplied (through pumps and water pipes). Like in the real world, some technologies are invented later than others are and so some only become available as your city ages.

After that it will be up to you to decide how to plan for the growth of your town. You might need an education system, city services, such as police or fire services and recreational amenities – frequently, your *Sims* will complain if they are missing a facility, or if you allow it too little money, and local newspapers will give valuable information.

Note: You must also link your town by road to the two towns on either side of yours (looking along the coastline) this will increase trade and therefore growth.

The Method:

1. Run the program *SimCity 2000*, if you have not carried on directly from Step One.

2. Use the *File* menu to 'Load a Saved City' and choose your city from the list of saved cities. Start at year *1900* and on *Easy* level.

3. Have a trial run to get to know the *City Toolbar*

(Figure 33.2) and the possibilities, without saving this attempt. This is *very important* so that you do not waste time later.

4. Click on *Neighbours Window* and make a note of the names and population sizes of your neighbouring settlements (you need to link to two of these).

5. Click on *Map Window* to get the basic structure of your city as it grows.

6. On some icons, click and hold the mouse button to get a sub-menu to select from. When locating for example, click and hold on *Power* and you can choose *Power Lines* or *Power Plants*, then click and hold on *Power Plant* and you will get a selection of technologies available at whatever date your city is at – select one then move to the map and click where you want to place it.

7. Only when you have enough facilities and power will the *Sims* start, of their own accord, to move into your city. You *Zone* areas, using the icons, and the *Sims* will construct their own appropriate buildings within these, as long as you also supply power, roads and water as well. Zone for *Residential* and, when all is well, the *Sims* will build their homes themselves. Zone for *Commercial Districts* and for *Industrial Districts* and they will eventually build shops and factories.

8. So, at its most basic:
   - zone for residential
   - zone for commercial
   - zone for industrial
   - build roads to link and surround the zones
   - build a power plant (careful of location!)
   - link it by power lines to all zoned areas (if a building flashes a power symbol, it needs power)
   - add water plants and supply lines

9. Then, use the other icons as necessary to add detailed facilities: schools, services like police and fire stations, railways and ports.

10. Many factors affect each other, for example –
    - Taxes may, or may not, induce industry and shops into your town
    - If your zones and facilities are too far apart, *Sims* may not travel
    - Without schools you may never get a

university as your *Sims* will not be well enough educated
- Power facilities and traffic may pollute as well as help growth, especially as they age
- Available technologies change through time
- Land values and taxes can affect your *Sims* behaviour
- Can bus systems alleviate traffic problems?
- Unemployment may occur if there are no jobs
- Your inhabitants need recreation too!

11. When you are happy, stop the program and run the simulation again from the start and properly attempt the decision-making exercise.

12. Stop the simulation after approximately 1–2 hour's play (excluding pauses), or until your city reaches a total population of 50,000 (the planned size for most early British New Towns after the Second World War).

Working Rules:

- you must use ONLY the *City Toolbar*, not the *Terrain Toolbar*
- do NOT USE the *Bulldozer* icon at the top of the toolbar
- ensure that the *No Disasters* switch is ON (from the *Disasters* menu at the top of the screen)
- you must not use any cheat codes
- you are not allowed to alter the physical landscape in any way, except to plant more individual trees
- you may *pause* (from the *Speed* menu) as much as you wish. (However, speed is important to rates of growth!)
- you must use *Save As* to save your city under your own name, NOT *Save* (as that would replace the original with your new version!), and save to both hard disk and to floppy disk, so that copies are available for discussion and later use.

(*Technical Note: If a group is using the same physical terrain, then the teacher could use Microsoft Windows to alter the attributes of the terrain file to prevent overwriting*)

STEP THREE: REPORT ON YOUR DECISION-MAKING

Write a full report to the Planning Authority on your planned New Town to include:

1. A full illustrated description of what happened to your town, what you did and why, the reports you received and the mistakes you made, during the simulation. Include an analysis of the population and state of financial health of your city at the end of your simulation period.

    - pause the simulation frequently so that you can use the general overall feedback provided: *graphs, budgets, newspapers, maps, land value, population, industry, ordinances* and *demand indices*
    - use the *Query* button to get information on particular blocks, tiles or buildings (you can even rename a school to your own institution's title)
    - use *Signs* to add particular names to buildings or areas to which you wish to draw attention
    - provide your final map of your town, either printed or saved to disk

2. An identification and explanation of the factors in the simulation which appeared to affect other elements of the simulation.

    Start by entering a '+' for a positive relationship and a '−' for a negative relationship in the Factor Matrix below (Figure 33.3).

3. Analyse the landscape you began with, and its effects on your town building. For example, which landscapes are good or bad for towns and how did different physical landscape elements interact with your Sims? (It is likely, for example, that they will build luxury homes rather than apartments near water – why?)

4. Suggest, from your answers to (1), (2) and (3), which general urban geographical models, concepts or theories may be operating and which may help to improve your results, if you ran the simulation again. Explain your choices.

5. Briefly:
    - describe how you could have improved your particular town building decisions
    - explain how you think your decision-making skills might be improved by using computer simulations like *SimCity 2000*.

NOTE:

If you do not have the full program, demonstration versions of SimCity 2000 are often included on computing magazine cover disks or CDs and the demo program can be downloaded from the Maxis Web site. The demonstration version if fully capable of running this exercise.

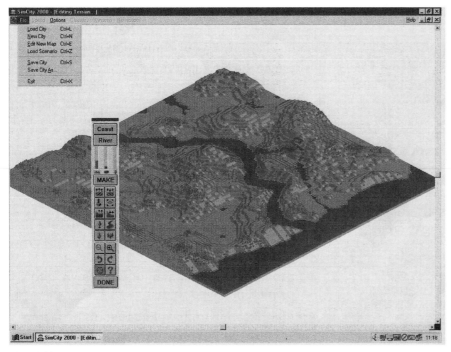

Figure 33.1

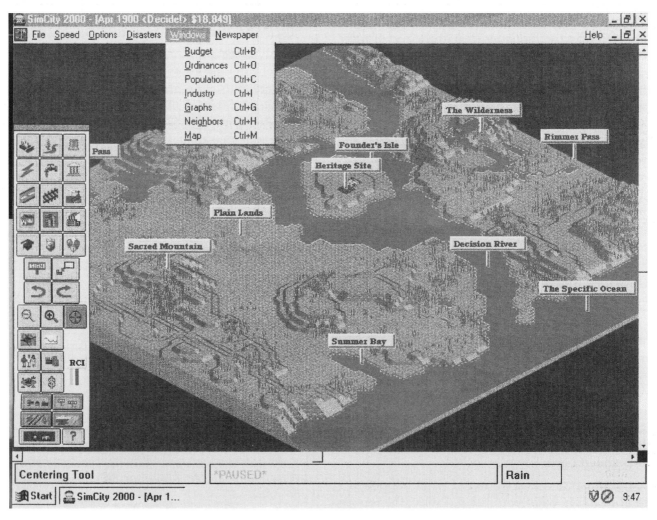

Figure 33.2

FACTOR MATRIX:

	land value	crime	pollution	traffic	population density	industry	commerce	residential population	life expectancy	education quotient	health	budgets
residential population												
commerce												
industry												
traffic												
pollution												
crime												
land value												
trees												
water												
distance from centre of town												
tax rates												
unemployment												
police												
fire services												
roads												
railways												
city ordinances												
education facilities												
electricity lines												
power stations												

Figure 33.3

Bibliography

The sources for decision-making still tend to concentrate upon the business, the political or the psychological aspects of making decisions. Very few books cover geographical problems and even fewer give methods appropriate to geographical decision-making. There are still no other texts which deal in any comprehensive way, and in depth, with the techniques specific to geographical decision-making.

Adair, J., *Effective Decision-Making* (Pan, 1985)

Adair, J., *Management Decision-Making* (Gower, 1985)

Barker, A., *How to be a Better Decision Maker* (Kogan Page Ltd, 1996)

Bracken, I., *Urban Planning Methods* (Methuen, 1981)

Burchell, R. W. and Listokin D., *The Environmental Impact Handbook* (Rutgers, 1985)

Carley, M., *Rational Techniques in Policy Analysis* (Heinemann, 1980)

Castles, F. G., Murray, D. J. and Potter, D. C., *Decisions, Organisations and Society* (Penguin, 1971)

Catlow, J., *Environmental Impact Analysis* (HMSO, 1981)

Chapman, M., *Decision Analysis Civil Service Handbook* (HMSO, 1980)

Chapman, M., *Plain Figures* (HMSO, 1986)

Cooke, S., and Slack, N., *Making Management Decisions* (Prentice-Hall, 1984)

Cornell, A. H., *The Decision-Maker's Handbook* (Prentice-Hall, 1980)

Cowlard, K. A., *Decision-Making in Geography* (First edition, Hodder and Stoughton, 1990)

Cuff, D. J. and Mattson, M. T., *Thematic Maps: Their Design and Production* (Methuen, 1982)

Curwin, J. and Slater, R., *Quantitative Methods for Business Decisions* (International Thomson Business Press, 4th edition, 1996)

Daly, M. T., *Techniques and Concepts in Geography* (Nelson, 1972)

Dargahi, N. and Bremer, M., *SimCity 2000: Power, Politics, and Planning* (Prima Publishing, 1995)

Dickinson, G. C., *Maps and Air Photographs* (Edward Arnold, 1969)

Dickinson, G. C., *Statistical Mapping and the Presentation of Statistics* (Edward Arnold, 1973)

Edwards, W. and Tversky, A., *Decision-Making* (Penguin, 1967)

Environmental Systems Research Institute, *Understanding GIS* (Longman, 1993)

Frenkiel, F. N. and Goodall, D. W., *Simulation Modelling of Environmental Problems* (Wiley, 1978)

Friend, J. and Hickling, A., *Planning under Pressure* (Pergamon, 1987)

Gilpin, A., *Environmental Impact Assessment* (EIA) (Cambridge U. P., 1995)

Glasson, J., Therival, R. and Chadwick, A., *Introduction to Environmental Impact Assessment* (U.C.L. Press, 1994)

Gowers, Sir E., *The Complete Plain Words* (HMSO, 1973)

Greenblat, C. S., *Designing Games and Simulations* (Sage, 1988)

Hall, P., *Great Planning Disasters* (Weidenfeld and Nicolson, 1980)

Hardingham, A., *How to Make Successful Decisions* (Sheldon Press, 1988)

Harrison, E. F., *The Managerial Decision-Making Process* (Houghton Mifflin, 1981)

Hay, I., *Communicating in Geography and the Environmental Sciences* (Oxford University Press, 1996)

Heirs, B., *The Professional Decision Thinker* (Grafton, 1989)

Hill, P. H. et al, *Making Decisions: A Multidisciplinary Introduction* (Addison-Wesley, 1987)

Hogarth, R., *Judgement and Choice* (Wiley, 1980)

Hogwood, B. M., and Gunn, L. A., *Policy Analysis for the Real World* (Oxford University Press, 1984)

Huber, G. P., *Managerial Decision-Making* (Scott Foresman, 1980)

Huxhold, W. E., *An Introduction to Urban Geographic Information Systems* (Oxford University Press, 1991)

Inman, K. and Swinburne, J., *Introduction to Flow Charting* (Polytech Publishers, 1972)

Jackson, K. F., *The Art of Solving Problems* (Teach Yourself, 1977)

Janis, I. L. and Mann, L., *Decision-Making – A Psychological Analysis* (Free Press, 1977)

Juniper, D. F., *Successful Problem Solving* (W. Foulsham & Co., 1989)

Kaufman, G. M., and Thomas, H., *Modern Decision Analysis* (Penguin, 1977)